A STILLNESS IN THE AIR

A STILLNESS IN THE AIR

by

Elisabeth Kyle

LONDON: PETER DAVIES

FIRST PUBLISHED 1956

PRINTED AND BOUND IN ENGLAND BY
HAZELL WATSON AND VINEY LTD
AYLESBURY AND LONDON

CONTENTS

Part One

PENSION SCHMOLKE

I

FRAU SCHMOLKE'S *pension* was in the Nürnbergerstrasse. I forget who recommended it to me, but I am quite sure (and indeed she told me later) that I would not have been accepted as a guest except for my profession. I must have mentioned it in my letter to her. No doubt she thought that a writer would make a change from so many artists and musicians.

Frau Schmolke was not in the least an arty person, nor did she encourage arty people to stay under her roof. But she had a love of music and a respect for the hard work which goes with making a living by the arts. There were a good many arty persons floating around the Berlin of the 'thirties, but most of them had private incomes to keep them afloat. Frau Schmolke kept her doorstep clear of such.

So I ought to have felt honoured by her taking me in. The taximan got the street door open for me, pressed a button which switched on a light, and then left me to carry my suitcase up myself. The staircase was enormously broad and so were the landings, each of which contained the entrance to two flats. It was quite dark, since there were no windows in this hollow core of the building. The light bulb swinging from its flex above each landing was certainly necessary. But I was just placing my foot on the first step of the third flight when all the lights—the two below me and the one above—went out.

I had not come across this economical way of lighting before. On entering from the street you press the button just inside the door, which switches on one light above each landing. But they only remain on for one minute. This is calculated to give you time to reach your destination, if you run hard. If you walk, you must take the risk of being plunged in darkness half-way up. If lucky enough to be on one of the landings already, you can feel for the button used by the flat dwellers there, and by pressing it gain another minute's illumination.

But the whole of Berlin had turned to blackness about me. I had travelled right through from London and had never been here before. I was tired. And now, to receive me, Berlin had clamped a large hand right over my face. Standing there, clutching the invisible rail, I almost screamed. Then a door opened suddenly. Somebody touched the button on the landing, and the four lights sprang to attention once more.

I didn't wait to see who had come out and was travelling downstairs. I rushed up the remaining flight, dragging my suitcase in case it happened again. And the light remained on long enough to read the words PENSION SCHMOLKE on the brass plate of the nearest door.

I rang the bell. The little maid who opened it seemed to expect me. "Willkommen!" she said, adding that Frau Schmolke had gone out of town for the day, but would I please follow her and she would show me my room?

A long, dark corridor, heavily furnished, ran down the middle of the *pension* like a spine. It smelt of wax polish and coffee grounds, and it had no outside lighting either. Berthe, the little maid, led me right to the end, where she threw open a door proudly, peeped in herself, and then drew back in dismay.

"Herr Jé!" she exclaimed.

The room was still occupied. A fair-haired young man stood in front of an easel painting busily, with some packed luggage at his feet. The room had two large windows facing the street, so there was plenty of light to see what was on the easel. It was a large poster design advertising some dentifrice. A girl with a flashing smile was riding a giant tube of tooth-paste over a boundless sea. The picture was almost finished but not quite.

The young man did not seem the least put out by my arrival. "Entschuldigen!" he said, smiling too. "I was told to be out of here hours ago, and of course everything is ready for you. The bed made up and so on. But this is a very important commission, and must be delivered this evening. It needs only a few more touches, as you can see. Will you be gracious enough to give me the further half-hour or so in which to make them?"

I bowed as graciously as I could and withdrew. Berthe was waiting for me in the passage. "The Fräulein can wait in the Speisezimmer," she said; adding, "It will soon be supper-time, anyway."

So, right at the start I obtained the clue to the running of the Pension Schmolke. Everything was in order, polished and clean. Meals were served at the proper times and a housewifely routine preserved. But the object of all this was to enable the artists who lived here to work as efficiently as possible. A musician must not be disturbed in his practising. A commercial designer must be allowed that extra half-hour or so to complete work in progress. And even I, as a travelling journalist, was already protected from noise by being given the room right at the end of the corridor, as far as possible from those furnished with pianos.

It was a very large room, well padded by its thick carpet and hangings of olive-green velvet. I think it must have contained the original dining-room furniture with which Frau and the late Herr Schmolke had started their married life; for there was a whole suite of chairs, tortuously carved in black oak to match the huge table and the enormous shelved cupboard in which I kept my clothes. Only the bed had been added, together with a blotting-pad and an already-opened bottle of ink, placed in the middle of the table. There was also, that night, a strong smell of the fixative used by the young man to ensure the removal of his still-wet poster without damage.

I unpacked and put my portable typewriter down on the table beside the bottle of ink. Amongst my supply of stationery was a new, thick diary. I had laid it out too, but now, on reflection, I pushed it into a drawer. I meant to write down in it full descriptions of all the people I met, and what they said; and perhaps some of them might be able to read English. I wanted to know just what the ordinary Berliner thought about the goings-on in his country just now. Perhaps in the end my diary might have to be kept locked up. . . .

Somebody tapped on the door. Frau Schmolke stood there,

dressed up a little because it was evening now, and perhaps to impress the new guest. She was a middle-aged woman of Wagnerian proportions, with grey hair and a double chin. She had an enormous amount of personality and an acute sense of humour. She greeted me kindly, but not in the least apologetically on account of my arriving tired and late and being kept out of my room. Either I could make allowances for the situation or I could leave.

"You will be able to work here, yes?" She pointed towards the table.

I reassured her. It was obviously the only thing she was anxious about. While under her roof, I must be able to do my work. "This room I generally keep for writers," she went on, "because it is far from the practising rooms of the musicians. Nothing here penetrates, except"—she paused, a reminiscent smile, almost a grin, carved her massive face in two—"except a trumpet, of course. *That* sound will penetrate anywhere."

As we walked down the corridor, she told me about the trumpet. Its owner played in a light orchestra, and, most unfortunately, had been given to practise an arrangement for trumpet of the "Prize Song" from the *Meistersingers*. The tones of this melody, practised for some hours every day, bored into the farthest corner of the Pension Schmolke, until Frau Schmolke felt bound to protest.

"I had to think of the other musicians under my roof," she said with a slight hint of apology, "for a trumpet can override everything, even that modern stuff Herr Paul plays by the hour. And they had also to do their practising, nicht?"

So the poor trumpeter was warned that he might be requested to leave. And in a desperate effort to avoid this, he hung out of the window of his room (my room) and practised into the street. Frau Schmolke, returning from a shopping expedition, found a small crowd gathered in the Nürnbergerstrasse and a policeman sauntering towards it from the other end of the street.

All the same, she told me, the poor man had really played the "Prize Song" very well—no bubbles or broken notes.

She threw open the door of the dining-room and ushered me in. A long table ran down the middle of it, covered by a course white cloth. The different ingredients of a cold supper dotted the cloth; herring salad, liver sausage, rough-hewn hunks of bread, and a great bowl of stewed fruit. The others had begun, but at our entry the men rose to their feet, napkins crumpled in one hand, and bowed.

"You had better seat yourself beside Herr Nicolai, who speaks such good English." Frau Schmolke indicated the empty seat on the left of a huge young man, well over six feet, whose bow had shown an Oriental fluidity lacking in the stiff inclinations from the Germans round about the table.

His surname had long been dropped and forgotten at the Pension Schmolke. The son of a rich Crimean landowner, he had fled from Russia after the Revolution, and earned a living by his rich velvety bass voice. Germany was short of good basses just then, and Nicolai found plenty of engagements. What Frau Schmolke coveted for him, however, was a steady job with some provincial opera company in Germany.

She said so kindly as we ate. Then her attention left us, and she did not hear me ask him if he would like that himself. "No," he said, "I would like to leave Germany altogether. I would like to go some place very far off; Australia perhaps."

I was surprised. It didn't seem to me that Australia would provide the same scope for an operatic bass. I asked him why he didn't go, and he looked sad and worried. "It is too difficult," he said, "because I only have a Nansen Passport. Like the other Russians who left our country in consequence of the Revolution, we forfeited the right to have one at all. Presently, as we found jobs in France and other countries, our position grew so complicated that we were issued with those temporary passports. And not every country likes them." He sighed heavily, passing me some cheese.

Besides Nicolai, there was a prematurely bald young man who trained the choir at the State Opera House; an Italian engineer; a Polish music teacher; a pale, withdrawn young woman who ate her meal in silence and then left the room before anybody else to practise Chopin two doors down the passage; and a middle-aged couple with whom Frau Schmolke appeared to be on especially friendly terms. The other guests were out for the evening.

"They, too, are professional musicians," Frau Schmolke informed me, running over their names. "One has a recital tonight"—she nodded towards a baize-covered board just inside the door, which was besprinkled with pinned-up programmes and concert intimations—"and I should, of course, have gone to it. But I have my own little card-party to go to this evening, and seeing that Paul's recital is satisfactorily booked——"

As soon as her attention was once more distracted, Nicolai told me, under his breath, about Frau Schmolke herself. Apparently her husband had been in quite a good position before the 1914 war. At the end of it, she was a widow with not a penny and only this handsome, old-fashioned flat and furniture left to her. By subdividing some of the rooms, she transformed it into a *pension*. Because of a passion for music, she had, from the first, aimed at a clientele of professional musicians; allowing them to practise their instruments (except the trumpet) and sitting lightly to irregular meal hours; so that, in a highly competitive trade, she had made her own niche and even created a legend.

"She *says* that she cultivates artists specially, because they don't notice food much," Nicolai finished; "but that is only her joke. We eat well, as you see."

In return, I told him how I hoped to pay for my meals with the money I would earn by writing about Germany, and perhaps other countries too. I had my newspaper connexions already and the appropriate German authorities had been most helpful. They had actually issued me with a Pass on their railways; and I was to call at the Berlin Headquarters of the Women's Central Organization, who would put me in touch with interesting things to write about.

"God help you!" Nicolai said.

The choirmaster grinned at me faintly across the table. "They will take you in hand, never fear!" he said. There seemed to be some sort of joke which ran right down the table until it reached Frau Schmolke, who killed it with a frown.

"Our German women are doing a noble work," she said, "and if they are a little too zealous——"

"I am glad to hear you say it," Nicolai interrupted her boldly, "for I am quite sure you detest Frau Scholtz-Klincke and her band just as much as we do."

Frau Schmolke suddenly smiled. Her smile and her long earrings combined made her look very like the Empress Augusta. "I detest too much organization," she said.

After supper I went to my room. I was tired. I unpacked, and then, opening the window, hung over the sill. As I was not a trumpeter, the stream of people continued along the Nürnbergerstrasse without pause. It was the time the theatres and opera houses would be going in, and all up Kurfürstendamm the cafés would be lit. The very air trembled with pleasure and excitement. So many plans, so much energy, so vast an ambition pervaded Berlin then that I am sure the street air carried them indoors triumphantly. I could feel them grazing my cheek.

THE Headquarters of the Women's Organization was housed in a handsome building which echoed with efficiency. A beautiful blonde woman, sitting at an immaculate desk, gave me their recipe for that.

"Only a short while ago we German women dissipated our energies through far too many channels," she said in a lecturing voice. "Just fancy, the Churches had their various organizations for women and young girls; the political parties did the same, and even small townships would muddle away collected funds by running their own little clubs for women! How much better it is that everything should be run from a central organization like this!"

"Did they all *want* to give up—I mean, join up?" I asked.

The blonde shrugged her plump shoulders. "Oh—in country places they are very conservative. There, I believe, they grumbled a little, especially the Church organizations, formed for some specific object, such as foreign missions. But how much better that *all* our funds—the funds of twenty million women, remember—should be administered in strict relation to the needs of the country!"

She then drew a typed paper out of a folder and glanced at its contents. "I have made arrangements for you to visit our Deutsches Heimat, and afterwards you must be at the building called Hibaudi, to see how we train our women in thrift and domestic economy. Also, here are two tickets for a performance of *A Midsummer Night's Dream* at our splendid Folks Theatre. You will be interested to hear the fine incidental music specially composed for it in place of Mendelssohn's old-fashioned tunes."

The Deutsches Heimat was a series of show-rooms housed not far off. It contained a fascinating exhibition of German furniture, hangings, and floor-coverings, all priced most moderately. Young couples, or brides accompanied by their mothers, drifted around, looking at the price tags, and now and then giving orders for replicas of whatever they admired. Everything was in simple, peasant style; very different from the heavy furniture and plush hangings of the Pension Schmolke. And the idea was, so far as I could see, to encourage home buying and simple living.

I went on to the huge building that bore its name, HIBAUDI, in large letters across the frontage. Its entrance was wreathed in swastikas and its outer hall decorated by large portraits of the nation's leaders. I took a good look at the one of Frau Scholtz-Klincke, Führerin of all the women's organizations in Germany. A surprisingly pretty woman of the blonde, Nordic type, with a crown of heavy plaits above her high, calm forehead. I could not myself see how she had helped to weld twenty million women into one vast body. Unless—was there a cold fanaticism in her gaze or did I only imagine it?

A pleasant young girl came forward to act as guide. The whole house, floor by floor, was planned to help housewives run their homes as economically as possible. Even the stair-treads were covered in different strips of linoleum or carpeting to show which would wear best. In one of the kitchens a demonstrator peeled some potatoes in the old, wasteful fashion, weighed them, showed us the result, and then contrasted that with the weight of potatoes peeled by a more modern gadget approved of by Hibaudi.

How to save fuel? Coffin-shaped baths narrowing half-way down, economized in the hot-water supply. Electric irons went into reverse so that you could boil kettles on them. And a whole room, lined with porcelain tiles, was given up to the encouragement of fish-eating. Dummy fish were laid out on slabs, ticketed with their names and the parts of Germany they came from, and appropriate recipes were framed and hung up above the slabs.

"Our nation must be weaned from too much meat-eating," said my guide in the slightly metallic voice of one who has learned her words off by heart. "Meat has to be imported often and, in any case, one wastes good soil if one gives it over to cattle-grazing."

The rooms glittered coldly, efficiently, as we walked past them, going downwards again floor by floor; treading first one strip of patterned linoleum and then a different pattern, so that the eye began to ache. Groups of mazed young women wandered about or passed one on the stairway, now and then bending double to examine the wear of one of the treads.

"They are profiting by our varied lessons in domestic economy," my guide said in satisfied tones.

"What made you think the lesson was necessary?" I asked; adding hastily, "We always understood at home that the German Hausfrau was adept at running a house."

She looked puzzled for a moment. Then her brow cleared. "It was the war. Such terrible times we had, when our women had no heart to pass on their domestic knowledge to their daughters! Many foods could not be got at all, so how could one learn to cook them? Then came the inflation, when money meant nothing, and one no longer kept household accounts or bothered to save. The women who are setting up house now—they were the neglected children of those years. Can you wonder they have to be taught?"

We were standing in the entrance now, right under the enlarged photograph of Frau Scholtz-Klincke. Sounds of Berlin's traffic came through the open doorway. I turned to shake hands.

"Have I helped you sufficiently for your article?" the young woman asked anxiously. "Is there anything else at all you would like?"

On an impulse I said, "Yes there is, please. I want to do some shopping, and I feel a slight headache coming on. You have not, by any chance, an aspirin you could give me?"

A warm, human look of sympathy flashed into her eyes at once. "Alas, no! I, too, suffer from Kopfschmerz, and used to carry aspirin always. But now we have been told that it is cowardly to avoid pain. If we possibly can, we must do without the drugs, which are so expensive, and so necessary for the hospitals and for real illness——"

"It doesn't matter," I said, "and thank you very much."

Once out in the air, I felt better. The trees in the Tiergarten had burst forth in layers of green leaves, and the children playing beneath them ran and shouted in an uninhibited and wasteful way. I watched them for a little, and then, extravagantly, hailed a taxi to drive me to the Unter den Linden. I could have walked there quite easily. But I found myself in the same frame of mind as Katherine Mansfield was when she said that prolonged living among the French had made her want to leave a pound of butter on the window-sill and let it melt in the sun.

The expensive shop windows along the Unter den Linden made me feel better every minute. Although early summer, it was warm enough already for tables to be set out before a little café up a side-street. I lunched, and then walked back to Braun's, close to the Hôtel Adlon, where I had noticed some rather chic hats in the window.

I needed a new hat, anyway. But fashion had made an about-turn, and my eye was not accustomed, as yet, to the new line. I liked one hat, but felt it might be too extreme. I told the saleswoman that I could not decide, but would come back for it if I wanted it.

They had lately uprooted the famous lindens which had lined the street and given it its name. That was because the petrol fumes of modernized and greatly increased traffic were poisoning the trees. The street, though magnificent, looked rather bald. I stared at a few more hats, both in shop windows and on the heads of the smarter women, and decided that the hat I had seen in Braun's, after all, was the one for me.

But I was really tired now, so when I had found my saleswoman and she had found my hat, it did not look nearly as becoming as I had remembered. However, I paid for it, put it on, and gave her my old one to make a parcel of. Then I started to leave the shop.

But in the little while I had been inside a crowd had gathered, lining the street on both sides from end to end. It was a quiet, well-behaved crowd, obviously waiting for some spectacle to pass down the middle of the street. It was being kept in place by a double row of helmeted police, spaced out at intervals. The whole scene was so like a London one when royalty was expected to pass by, that for a moment I could not quite identify the jarring note.

It was simply that the policemen stood, not with their backs to the crowd but facing it, each with one hand on the holster which held his gun.

There was a roar and a rattle as an armoured car dashed up the middle of the Unter den Linden. Men with tommy-guns were mounted on the running-board, and they had scarcely passed when another car, less obtrusive but driving very quickly on the heels of the first, passed by. I might scarcely have noticed the stiff figure standing up in it with hand outstretched, except for the suddenly galvanized action of the crowd.

"HEIL Hitler! HEIL Hitler!" it roared, and swung its right hand up.

Not wanting martyrdom, I swung my right hand upwards too. My fingers brushed the trimming of my new hat, paused, then fingered it. I knew now why it hadn't seemed so becoming as when I had first tried on the hats in Braun's. The one I had liked then had had a band of velvet round the crown. This felt like Petersham. . . .

I turned and re-entered the shop. The sales girls still clustered about its windows, peering into the street. I had difficulty in regaining the attention of the one who had served me. But she seemed to understand what I wanted quickly enough, for she disappeared into a cupboard and came out again with what at first sight looked like a replica of the hat I had on.

Only the twist of fabric about its crown was different; that and the subtle line of an original model. The open cupboard revealed a shelf full of copies like the one I had on. We made the exchange, with no apologies offered on either side. I went home, triumphant and refreshed, to meet Frau Schmolke travelling along the corridor like a stately ship.

"You look as though you had had a successful day," she re-

marked. So I told her about my new hat, and that reminded me
to mention having seen the Führer. It was thanks to him, I said,
that, on putting my hand up to my hat, I realized that I had
been fobbed off with the wrong one.

I remember now the strange look that came over her face.
"Then he indeed brought you luck!" she said.

That must have been the night Gertrud Orff arrived at the
pension. She was fair, fat, and middle-aged, and an old friend
of Frau Schmolke's. Her only beauty lay in her eyes, which
were still amazingly lustrous; almost violet coloured with velvety pupils. When she looked at you and opened them wide,
you forgot the folds of pasty flesh in which they were embedded.

Gertrud had had some small reputation as a singer of Lieder
and of what is rather repulsively known as Art songs. There was
nothing affected about her, however, or she would have been
no friend of Frau Schmolke's. From the way all the other guests
beamed when she plumped down in her seat at supper, it was
obvious that she had stayed here many times before and that
they all liked her.

"Guard thy voice with a muffler, lieber Nicolai!" she be-
sought him as he hurriedly excused himself on account of an
open-air concert at which he was singing. "Remember, once it
has gone it has gone! Like mine." She helped herself to a large
spoonful of herring salad without the slightest appearance of
regret.

"Now, Gertrud," Frau Schmolke tried to speak convincingly,
though honesty made her protest sound weak, "thou knowest
thy voice——"

"Is no longer able fully to interpret as it should." The singer
munched unconcernedly through her words. "So all that remains is to teach my interpretations to others."

"Gertrud will make a fine teacher!" Her friend spoke more
warmly. "She will gather enough pupils about her almost at
once."

I felt drawn to Gertrud. As the meal was almost finished and
the performance at the Folks Theatre started quite soon, I drew
out my spare ticket, laid it on the cloth, and asked if anyone

would like to accompany me and make use of it? I managed
to catch Gertrud's eye as I spoke, and felt enormously relieved
when she beamed and thanked me, picking up the cardboard
square with fingers much longer and more sensitive than one
would have expected from her face.

The Folks Theatre had once been Reinhardt's Theatre of
the Five Thousand and the scene of his lavish spectacles. On his
fall from grace, the new régime in Germany took over the building as a place of entertainment for the People. I had almost said
the Party, because you had to show your membership card before you could buy a ticket. Theoretically, non-members of the
Social-Democratic Party could take seats for a performance if
there were any left. Practically, there never were, as each seat
cost only sixpence, and the best seats went to those who booked
first.

Thus the circus went along with the bread. The cost of first-
rate productions was borne by the State, since the trifle charged
for the seats went no distance at all. Gertrud told me as we went
along that the Folks Theatre was Goebbels' special baby, and
that he had had the good sense to nominate as manager-pro-
ducer Walther Brugmann, a brilliant young man from Leipzig.
However, it appeared that the elaborate lighting system and the
original staging of some of the older pieces were left-overs from
Reinhardt's reign; although nothing was said about that.

"Herr Goebbels had hoped to provide a stage for a new
school of German dramatists; but unfortunately they have not
been forthcoming, so we have had to fall back on Schiller and
Goethe—and Shakespeare, of course!" Gertrud commented
dryly as we approached the floodlit exterior of the theatre.
"Last time I was in Berlin, I went to see a new arrangement of
Ibsen's *Peer Gynt* done by one of our fine young dramatists. No
doubt he was a special friend of Herr Goebbels and no doubt
Ibsen's own play is rather depressing. But the arrangement was
terrible!"

She said all this loudly as we entered the foyer. I hoped no
one had heard, but the badly dressed and perspiring crowd pouring through it paid no attention whatever to us. They were quite

obviously the People for whom Goebbels had planned this entertainment, and any members of the audience who belonged to a slightly different stratum took pains to laugh as loudly, take up as much room, and dress as badly as the others, so as to escape any remark.

Gertrud herself was wearing thick woollen stockings, although she had put on a sapphire blue velvet dress in my honour. I think she had borrowed a pair of long ear-rings too; at least, the ones she was wearing looked very like those worn by her friend Frau Schmolke the night before. But I believe the stockings were a pure oversight and not an attempt to blend in with the mob. At any rate, she did not trouble to modify the tones of her clear and beautiful voice as she told me what she thought of the purely Aryan music which has dispossessed Mendelssohn's lovely tunes.

But the play itself was put on with great magic and artistry. Titania came gliding down-stream on a giant water-lily to keep her tryst. After the curtain fell on the last scene, in the Duke's banqueting hall, it rose again for a moment, to give a glimpse of the empty disorder, the wreaths flung down by vanished guests, the flickering lamps; and the great door opening slowly while Puck turned backward on its threshold with a last grimace, and the full, round Athens moon shone in the strip of sky behind him.

"Reinhardt's idea, that floating water-lily!" Gertrud hissed in my ear. "And that final effect is his, too, if I remember rightly. But I'll ask Walther when we go behind. He's honest and he'll tell me."

I got my first shock when we went behind the scenes. The stage, robbed of its fabulous lighting effects, looked a tawdry tangle of felt and cardboard. The great silvery water-lily which had seemed to give off an iridescent sheen of its own, now lay spread out, grey with dirt and only half concealing the mechanism which had moved it. Gertrud stepped over everything disdainfully, followed by the Leipzig producer, who seemed to be an old friend of hers and who had invited us both to come out and have a drink with him.

So we three walked down the Kurfürstendamm, now, at this time of night, a broad alley of pleasure, lit by the illuminated show-cases lining the kerb. Like oblong cubes of ice, those glass show-cases contained luxurious and expensive hand-bags, costume jewellery, or whatever was stocked by the shops behind them. Round the base of each one was a circle of bedded-out plants, their faces turned up towards the light which illuminated them from above. It was nearly midnight, but the cafés were full and the music of half a dozen small orchestras warred with each other across the street.

When we entered one, the manager came forward to greet us. Apparently he was an old friend of the producer, who could hardly wait to tell him of the difficulties of his new post. Loudly they lamented the edict against Mendelssohn's incidental music to the *Dream*; and scathingly they spoke of Herr Nick's uninspired substitutes. They spoke in German, too, and I could not help glancing anxiously about me, lest this open scorn of the Führer's protégé got us into trouble.

But nobody seemed to mind. The minute orchestra of the café went on playing Strauss waltzes, while the pavement outside echoed to the footfalls of the strolling crowd.

3

I WAS enjoying myself so much in Berlin, I quite forgot to look
for a letter from Professor Aspasia Rauert. When it came, I
stared down at the strange stamp, and the postmark, Riga,
without for the moment remembering.

It lay on my plate one morning when I came in for lunch.
Nicolai, the big Russian who sat next me at meals, picked it
up, stared at the stamp and laughed. "All their new, pretty
little stamps," he exclaimed, but quite without bitterness;
"when before the war Latvia and the others made do with a
picture of the Russian eagle. . . ."

"Latvia and the others" meant the new states, Latvia,
Estonia, and Lithuania, which before the war had been Russian
provinces. Now they were sovereign republics, each run by a
small but enthusiastic peasant population which had promptly
disowned everything Russian. Someone in London had given
me an introduction to Professor Rauert of Riga, the new capital
of Latvia. I had thought that the Baltic states, or at least one of
them, would prove more novel, from the journalist's point of
view, than the Balkan states with which they were so often confused. So I had written to Professor Rauert, suggesting a visit
to Riga and asking her for the address of some modest hotel.

Her letter told me that she would be out of town for the first
week or so of my visit, but would hope to see me when she came
back. As for hotels, why bother about them when her own comfortable flat stood empty, with her Russian maid Vera "sitting
there eating her head off"? If I liked to pay for my board, I
was welcome to use it, and to stay on as paying guest after she
came back.

I let Nicolai read the letter. He tossed it back to me. "You
mean to go?"

"Yes. It will be interesting. And the nearest I shall ever get to Russia, I suppose."

"Oh—it was in the Empire, but it was never properly Russian. The peasants belonged to a different breed, with a language that looked and sounded like nothing on earth. As for the upper classes—the big landowners—they might have Russian patents of nobility and attend the court at St Petersburg, but they all came of German stock."

"German?" I looked surprised.

He nodded. "They are all descended from the old Prussian Order of Knights of the Sword, who colonized Latvia and brought their version of Christianity to it. They have always remained German in speech and sympathy. I used to hear it said that their influence at court was pro-German during the war and that the Tsarina favoured them too much. She was a German, too, you know."

The others had begun to file in for lunch. Nicolai, who had adopted German customs at least partially, wrapped his napkin round his neck, tying it into rabbits' ears at the back of his head. It was remarkable how, in spite of that, he managed to retain a faintly elegant appearance. He plunged his spoon into his soup, and ate until presently I interrupted him to ask another question.

"What has happened to them now? The German Balts, I mean."

"Their estates were divided and most of the land given over to the Latvian peasants after 1918. They are greatly impoverished, and have had to take jobs in Riga and other biggish towns."

I asked next if there were many of them, compared with the Latvian population. He looked around cautiously, to make sure that everyone else was talking and could not hear us. Then he dropped his voice as he answered, "Too many. I don't know the figures exactly, but if they numbered only a few hundreds, they will still prove too many for the Latvians. Of that I am quite convinced. The Balts are an able, educated people with a strong sense of being the Master Race. They are very near the frontier of Germany; near their brothers of the Reich. And the Latvian people number only two millions, after all."

I looked at him, puzzled. But just then the door opened to allow two new guests to enter. Everyone stopped talking while Frau Schmolke performed the introductions. "Herr and Frau Bennett all the way from America, my friends! Herr Bennett comes here to study singing under our friend Karl Wolff."

They were both very young and evidently just recently married. Their youth did not strike me then, of course, since I shared it myself. But now (coming upon their names in my diary) I see their two figures sitting down shyly at Frau Schmolke's table. I take a quick look at them over my plate, as everyone else is doing. He has an American hair-cut and a nice, open face. She is not pretty, but is well pulled together by her clothes, and seems like being good fun. The polite, formal silence following an introduction in Germany is soon broken. But I can see, and hear, nothing more of that first arrival.

Except, I remember, they at once got friendly with the sandy-haired man known jocularly as the Fliegender Holländer. The Bennetts had not yet had time to acquire any German, and the Dutchman spoke colloquial English without any accent whatever. Frau Schmolke had told me his story quite soon after his arrival.

He suffered from asthma in so acute a form that it was impossible for him to live anywhere except on sandy soil and almost at sea-level. Holland has plenty of sea-level but too much sea air, and so, being of independent means, he spent most of his time wandering from one inland city to another, as near to the centre of Europe as he could get.

He had a wife, to whom he was devoted. Soon after their marriage, however, his wife developed T.B., and had, for some years now, just managed to keep alive in a sanatorium high up in the Swiss Alps. For her husband to visit her there was impossible. He could only have succumbed to one choking fit of asthma after another. Every few months, therefore, her doctors permitted her to descend half-way down the mountain, while his allowed him to meet her half-way up it. There, in a *chalet-*

pension perched between heaven and earth, they would spend a few days together before parting once more. I must say, however, that he concealed his loneliness very well, or possibly mitigated it by indulgence in the cheerful companionship found at the Pension Schmolke.

It was the Dutchman who suggested to the Bennetts and myself that we should visit Haus Vaterland together. This was one of the most popular of the lower-priced pleasures of Berlin under the Third Reich. The Bennetts had brought their own little car over with them to Europe. The night before I left Berlin we drove in it to the huge building with HAUS VATERLAND in electric letters across its roof. We paid our entry money, and then stood in the main hall studying the list of attractions offered on every floor.

It was a high building, and each floor contained a different restaurant with a different speciality or cachet. The Dutchman had been here before. He said the thing to do was to tackle as many as possible by having a different course in each. Actually, we had eaten our usual supper at the *pension*, because it was paid for already in the weekly bill. So all we felt like having was hot dogs at the Wild West Bar.

The lift shot us upward. We were decanted just at the entrance to an apparent log cabin, where a cowboy in sheepskin chaps and sombrero lounged realistically against the bar. We bought and ate our hot dogs, but the Dutchman waved away all offers of beer to accompany them. "Much better fun to have a glass of wine in the Viennese Restaurant," he suggested, "and then perhaps a cup of Mocha in the Turkish Café to end up with."

But we didn't get to the Viennese Restaurant at once, because on the way out the two men caught sight of the shooting-gallery. "Gosh! We'll never get them past that!" Clare Bennett whispered. Nor did we.

Her husband did pretty well. Then came the Dutchman's turn. He picked up the gun negligently, and without even sighting properly scored a bull. Of course it was just pure accident, but we applauded politely. He grinned, fiddled about with the gun in his left hand and somehow scored another. When it happened a third time, the man in charge of the shooting gallery handed him a stuffed monkey, which was promptly bestowed on me.

During the next ten minutes or so, I was given an assorted selection of prizes, all of which the Dutchman said I might keep. There was a huge china vase, I remember, which I secretly gave back to the stall keeper when the winner's back was turned. There were two large dolls and another monkey. Clare wouldn't take any of them, and I finally moved towards the lift with my arms full.

John Bennett was looking pop-eyed. "Say! Where did you learn to do that?"

"Oh," said the Dutchman, "it's about the only sport I *am* allowed to indulge in. Not much physical exertion, you know. Actually, I hold the amateur shooting championship of Holland."

We followed him in a sort of respectful haze into the Viennese Restaurant. I thought John Bennett looked a little cross, but he was very good-natured and soon cheered up. I dare say he reminded himself that, at any rate, he could sing.

The atmosphere on this floor was very different. Shaded lights beamed on the little tables in their alcoves, and the air throbbed to a waltz played by an orchestra at the far end of the room. One whole wall of the restaurant was frescoed from end to end with a representation of the Danube meandering past the vineclad hills outside Vienna. The sky above the water was pin-pricked with stars; and by some mechanical means a tiny river-boat moved along the stretch of river, its jewelled lights travelling right across the wall.

The Bennetts sighed with delight. I felt sure they would rather have finished the evening alone, but the head waiter had shown us to a table for four; so what could we do? A quiet and luscious dreaminess enfolded us. Even the Dutchman remained silent, listening to the waltz. They brought us a great Sachertorte, laden with whipped cream. A waiter came with the wine, held in a curious glass globe rather like a coffee machine; but we knew it could not be the first, new pressing of the grapes which is thus served in Vienna, because that happened in autumn, and it was still early summer here in Berlin.

I looked longingly at the coffee laced with whipped cream being served at the next table. But the Dutchman shook his head. "If you take that," he said, "you won't want the real Turkish coffee they serve on the next floor. And you will miss the opportunity of seeing something more."

The dummy river-boat had turned, and was busily nosing up the painted stream on the wall when we walked past it reluctantly on our way out. The beat of the waltz faded behind us as we went down to the floor below. Here the setting was dramatically changed. We stepped immediately from the staircase into a Turkish mosque; or rather, Oriental pavilion, for mosques don't usually have red-plush divans deposited in alcoves round the walls.

A boy—a real little Turk or Moor, I'll swear—came tripping towards us on the toes of his curled-up shoes. He wore wide scarlet trousers, and, by some trick of mirrors, appeared to be approaching through an endless vista of arches dripping with stalactites of wood carving. He salaamed, departed, and returned with the eggcupfuls of strong black coffee in their brass containers. There was no sound, as we sipped our coffee, except the drip-drip of the fountain in the middle of the court. No music now, and only a hushed murmur of voices from the other alcoves half hidden by the fretwork of the pillars on each side of them.

"If they had bothered to stage a Latvian Restaurant, you wouldn't have had to leave Berlin at all," the Dutchman said to me.

The young Bennetts looked at one another, mystified. "Latvia, where's that?" they asked.

It was a little after midnight when we left Haus Vaterland. The night was so warm and fine, the streets were still crowded with late audiences from the theatres and opera reluctant to go home. John ran the car right down the Unter den Linden, for us to enjoy the brilliant illuminations in honour of Mussolini's state visit. Golden tridents lined the streets, and the bronze horses galloping above the Brandenburger Tor glowed in a greenish light.

It was like Reinhardt's *Dream* only bigger and better. This production took the whole of Berlin for its stage, and the audience were the actors too. Not one, but a dozen orchestras sent out appealing phrases as we drove past the open doors of the cafés. There was a constant change of key, of course; but that always happens with music heard in a dream.

"Say, isn't this wonderful?" Clare Bennett twisted her neck right round, almost, to get a last glimpse of the galloping green horses against the sky.

The Dutchman had been very silent. Now he said one word, "Kitsch."

"What do you mean, Kitsch?"

"Oh, it's a slang word. It means, well, just a little false. Contrived—I know, in America you would say phoney."

We didn't argue with him. Considering his health and his own private sorrow, it was understandable that waves of dissatisfaction should come over him from time to time and force him to make cynical remarks. I felt, suddenly, very mature and understanding, and I'm sure the two Bennetts felt the same.

Part Two

DOWN THE MOSCOW ROAD

4

THE taxi drove quickly through the modern part of Riga, stopping at the entrance to a block of flats on a wide, handsome boulevard. Olga, Professor Rauert's Russian maid, held the door of one of the ground-floor flats open for me. She was a heavy, sleepy-looking woman with a few words of broken German and a welcoming smile. I was thankful that she was expecting me, for I was very tired. It had been a long journey from Berlin.

I was so tired I didn't even notice the couple of rooms she led me through. From her gesture, the second one seemed to be put at my disposal as a sitting-room. A small bedroom opened directly off it. A jug of hot water stood ready on the washstand, draped by a towel.

Olga laid down my two suitcases. "If the Fräulein will wait a little," she said in her queer German, "I will some coffee prepare."

By the time I had washed and changed I felt better. I looked around the little bedroom. Then I stepped out of it into the sitting-room, and looked around that. I knew something about my hostess by repute, and the furnishing of these two rooms bore out my imaginary picture of her. She must be middle-aged at least, for she had graduated at the University of Petersburg, but had gone back to the provinces to keep house for her father, who was judge of the district round Kieff. The decoration of these two rooms showed clearly what Aspasia Rauert had come from.

Nicolai had told me that the legal profession did not stand as high in Russia as it did in Britain. He had described how, in his country and in others too, an ambitious small-town attorney might become a judge by the simple method of passing the right examination. The Professor's taste leaned to yellow walls, chairs upholstered in green moquette, and a quantity of photographs, framed and enlarged. Her desk was the only non-committal thing in the room. It was built for work, and laden with papers all neatly arranged in folders. On one side of the desk lay her abacus, or counting machine of coloured balls strung on wires. I had only seen them used in kindergartens at home. Here in Riga, I was to see them in use in shops, banks, private houses; a last relic of the old Russian ways.

I was fingering the abacus when Olga appeared in the doorway announcing that coffee was ready. She led me back into the first room leading off the hall, the one I had crossed on my arrival. I could now see that it served both as dining-room and as some sort of link between the two rooms I had just left, and also led to another suite, shut off by a door at the end of it. But it was furnished so differently, breathed so different an air, that I felt as I had when we stepped out of the Haus Vaterland lift, too suddenly transported from one climate to another.

I stood gazing about me, bewildered. The furniture here was old and fine. Worn but exquisite Persian rugs strewed the polished floor, an Empire sofa stretched across one wall under a family portrait, while a crystal chandelier of great elegance dropped its lustres over the marble inlay of the table on which the coffee-tray was set. I walked over to it and picked up the coffee-pot. It was of fine, thin silver with a crest surmounted by a coronet on its side, and the same coronet showed on the corner of the linen napkin laid across my plate.

Olga's eyes followed me from the door. She was saying something that sounded like, "The Professor forgot to leave me the keys of her cupboards. I was forced to borrow the coffee-pot and the napkin from the Herr Baron."

It sounded like gibberish, so I sat down and poured myself out some coffee. Olga vanished. Through the window, beyond the two faded silk curtains which masked it, I could hear all the traffic of the boulevard outside. Not only cars and buses, but now and again the jingling of harness as an ancient droshky, another left-over from Russian days, went by.

Inside the room, however, it was very quiet. So quiet, that

the sound of a door opening at its farther end startled me as if a pistol had been let off. There, with the sunlight from the other room shining behind him, stood a man, watching me. He looked about forty; small, square, and tough. When he saw I had noticed him, he stepped forward, bowing.

"Let me introduce myself. Baron Pilar von Smichow. Olga tells me you are an English friend of the Professor's?"

"I'm afraid I'm using your coffee-pot," I said hurriedly, "and your napkin. I'm so sorry." (But where had he come from? The Professor hadn't mentioned that anyone else lived here.)

He bowed again. "Not at all. Very happy to have been able to help Olga out in a difficulty. As a rule, I am in the country at this time of year, but my plans had to be altered at short notice, and I returned this morning. So very sorry Doctor Rauert did not inform you of her absence. But of course, if you mean to stay in Riga for any length of time, I am at your disposition. I can inform you about hotels——"

If he kept his linen and silver here, then this must be his home as well as the Professor's. But to make sure, I asked him. It was odd that she had never mentioned his name. And yet, from all I heard, she didn't seem to be the kind of person . . .

The Baron sat down on one of his own chairs and went on talking. He spoke English fluently, with a slight guttural accent. On the surface, he seemed perfectly at ease, but underneath it one sensed perturbation. I suspected it was caused by me.

"Doctor Rauert and I share this flat," he was saying, "though only in a manner of speaking, of course. She has her own apartments, I have mine. This room and the hall are no man's land, but I had more furniture than she, so my family pieces are disposed in them. This serves as our joint dining-room, for by sharing our meals and Olga's wages we both economize. It may be said that we see one another only at meals."

"Oh, quite," I said hastily. "The two suites are so far apart, I won't trouble you at all. And I'm very good at finding my own way about strange cities."

"I fear that Olga may not be able to look after you properly," suggested the Baron. "I really think you would be much
more comfortable in an hotel."

He was so very anxious to get rid of me, I can't think why I
did not go. Ordinarily, I would not have stayed five minutes
after so broad a hint. But the good hotels in Riga were frighten-
ingly expensive, and Doctor Rauert had warned me, in her first
letter, against going to any except the best. She, at any rate, had
seemed quite glad to rent me her part of the flat. So I stiffened.

"Olga seems quite prepared to look after me," I told him;
adding, "It's so much nicer being in a private house than in an
hotel, don't you think?"

He looked at me dubiously. "How long do you intend to stay
in Riga?"

"About a fortnight," I answered, pouring myself out some
more coffee from his silver pot.

He thought a moment, obviously adapting himself to the
situation. At last he said briskly, "Very well. You had better
leave housekeeping questions in my hands, as you will not
understand them here. Olga cannot, of course, be expected to
cook two separate series of meals. Coffee she can bring to your
room in the morning, whenever you ring for it. Lunch suits me
best at one o'clock, and dinner at seven. You can eat Russian
food?"

"I can eat anything."

"Good. Because Olga knows only the Russian cuisine, and I
prefer it myself. I have an office job in town, so I must occupy
the bathroom first. After nine o'clock it is entirely at your disposal. I hope you will be comfortable here."

With another bow he left me. I caught a glimpse of his own
sitting-room as he passed into it. The sunlight caught the gilding on the French furniture, and the rose silk curtains blew in
a little with the draught. Then the door closed with finality, and
I was left alone.

The Professor did not turn up for a week. During that time I
explored the streets of Riga, and mollified the Baron at meal-
times so that he prolonged them in order to give me information

regarding what I should see and do. Having, like other German Balts, lost most of his property on the founding of the new republic, he worked as a clerk in a travel office. His family heirlooms were all that remained of his old life; that, and his scorn of Latvia's new régime.

He wanted me to confine my sight-seeing to the relics of Riga's Hanseatic past, from the Church of St Peter with the largest wooden spire in Europe, to the magnificent House of Blackheads, the meeting-place of a fifteenth-century guild of German traders who took for their symbol the head of the negro St Mauritius. All that was very interesting. Most admirable, too, were the broad boulevards, the modern Americanized public buildings and the handsome, glittering shops.

But what really fascinated me were the few traces of old Russian days left behind from the time when Riga was one of the greatest ports of the Empire. It was difficult to find them. Not difficult, of course, to find the gigantic Russian cathedral. After that, the most universal mark left on Riga's ordinary everyday life was the eternal click-clack of the abacus beads. Saleswomen in shops, clerks in offices, merchants at their desks, all moved the coloured beads up and down on their wires with amazing flexibility, arriving at the answer to intricate sums much more quickly and surely than by pencil and paper calculations.

As for the Russians themselves, there seemed very few of them about. True, there was the Black Exchange, which operated openly down the whole length of the street known as Smitsu Iela, and which was mostly in the hands of Russian Jews. If you strolled along it past the Bourse, and stopped for a moment to look at a shop window, a hand was laid on your arm and a voice asked in your ear if you had any English pounds or American dollars. . . .

And there were the Russian gypsies. One sometimes saw them running by the side of their riderless, unclipped horses, which they hoped to sell in the market. Riga's huge market had been famous for centuries. It still swarmed over several streets and squares in all its exotic variety. Its heart was the huge

covered hall in the middle of the city. On market-days, long
before dawn, all the country roads leading towards Riga were
choked with carts bringing in produce. From very early in the
morning, the streets and lanes around the big hall would have
blossomed with booths, while empty carts and weary, tethered
horses stood all down the middle of the street.

I liked to visit the fish-market inside the hall. Here were enormous glass tanks, in which every variety of northern sea-fish re-
volved slowly, alive and horribly active. Presiding over them
was an attendant armed with Neptune's trident. The Riga
housewives would themselves revolve round the outside of the
tanks, presently making their decisions. Then down plunged
the trident, and the chosen fish would be brought out, impaled
and still wriggling.

The dairy stalls showed wooden kegs of primrose-shaded
butter; soft sheeps' cheese; and a curious titbit much appre-
ciated by the humbler citizens for its cheapness, which seemed
to be made of flour and flax-seed oil rolled into little balls. The
bare-armed dairy women were all Latvians, for dairy farming is
among their talents. But the heaped-up vegetable stalls were in
the charge of Russians, since the small Russian colonies and villages still remaining in Latvia specialized in market gardening.

The Jews were in control of the junk market. This was perhaps the most fascinating section of all. It was held outside the
hall, in a narrow lane closed at the farther end by a barrier of
empty carts. The cobbles of the lane were strewn with mounds
of scrap. Grotesque figures bent over them, prodding and sift-
ing, dragging out some length of rusted chain, examining the
links, then letting it fall with a clatter back on the heap. . . .

Up and down each side of the lane were trestle-tables laden
with still more junk. Yet here one would sometimes come across
a relic of Riga's more aristocratic, if alien, past. Sometimes an
old copper samovar would turn up, battered and dirty but still
of good shape. The modern Latvian had no use for any such
reminder of the Russian way of living. There was, however,
something to be said for them as the means of providing an
endless supply of hot tea. You lit the charcoal lamp, and when

the water was boiling, you dipped a bagful of tea-leaves into the interior of the samovar, pulling it out again by its attached string when you thought the tea was sufficiently strong. You could leave the lamp burning for hours, and ensure a supply of boiling hot tea, unspoiled by tannin bitterness, whenever you chose.

And then, occasionally, one might come upon a branched candelabrum carved out of wood and still showing traces of former gilding. Those wooden candelabra, carved out in some Russian forest to decorate the castle of the owner of the forest, had not been made since before the Revolution. The Baron shook his head when I told him of my two finds.

"Probably stolen by the gypsies," he said. "These are typical old country-house pieces. Had their owners troubled to bring them away, they would have found that the antique dealers give quite good prices for such things nowadays. But many of my friends, like myself, have had to leave their old homes for want of means to keep them up. If they are left standing empty, the gypsies break in and take anything they can find."

It was now high summer, and the city had grown almost unbearably hot. But a curious little affair, half tram, half railway, led out of it and traversed what was known as Riga-Strand; a series of linked watering-places right on the edge of the Baltic. I would board this train when I wanted a breath of air and would presently leave it at some primitive platform sanded over with the fine white sand of the Baltic coast. On one side of me, the great pine forests stretched inland, scenting the air. On the other would curve an esplanade with the sparkle of the water beyond.

I would take the sandy path winding down to the sea. The young pines shaded it, and the seaside villas bordered it, dumped down here and there just casually, without any straight lines or planning. Sometimes the little path would run right beneath some white-painted verandah where people lazed or hung over the rails, smoking. Sometimes the pine trees bore home-made advertisements of this boarding-house or the other, with directions how to get there. Occasionally a gay little hut would display holiday trophies for sale : hand-woven scarves or carved, painted toys.

And then, suddenly, round the side of some villa or past some thick clump of trees, one would come on the long, dark line of the Baltic Sea. A few of the larger resorts would have hemmed it in with a stretch of esplanade. Beehive chairs stretched out in a long row, their high backs turned to the wind. Arc lamps stood at intervals down the esplanade, prepared to floodlight it after dark; and loud-speakers stood ready to pour soft music into the ears of the sitters upon the beehive chairs, drowning the sound of the sea.

But there were no such refinements at the little place I liked best. It was called Edimbourg, having been named long ago, in the old Russian days, to commemorate the marriage of the Tsar's daughter to Queen Victoria's son, the Duke of Edinburgh. Down almost at the water's edge stood an enormous, elaborate palace made apparently of sugar-icing, and once a royal holiday home. Now it was a convalescent hospital, but still too big for the place. Otherwise, there was nothing; nothing at all except a few villas perched on the dunes, and the great pine forest stretching inland, where that fabulous monster, the elk, still roamed.

One curious thing struck me about the long stretch of white sand embracing the line of the coast. No matter how warm and beautiful the day was, no matter how still the sea, one never saw bathers there. Strollers, paddlers, sand-castle-builders, yes. But no bathers, in spite of the shallow safety of that part of the coast. The reason lay in the Latvian love of nature—complete nature, untrammelled by bathing-suits of any description. Bathing hours along the coast were limited to a few hours very early in the morning. The stretches of sand were reserved for male bathers from eight to nine, and for female from nine to ten. After that people left the water alone.

But the children went as near to it as they could, eagerly turning over the tangled heaps of seaweed and the wrack from the last storm; searching for—what? For amber, they told me. A great reef of amber lay under the sea just here. After any big storm, there was always the possibility that bits might have been broken off and, caught in a lump of seaweed, thrown on the shore.

True, this was not the season of storms. But the children were always hopeful. Back in Riga, the shops would give you a good price for a lump of amber. The jewellers along the Smitsu Iela were full of amber objects to tempt the tourist; long ropes of it, cigarette-holders, little carved figures or pear-shaped ear-rings on lengths of gold chain.

Every country had its own preference, a jeweller told me. German tourists liked the pale yellow amber, which is what it looks like when first polished, before it deepens with age. The English preferred it mellowed to orange-brown, and for that reason would rather search the antique shops, whose windows I have seen festooned with ropes more than a hundred years old. But the French liked their amber necklets cut into many facets so that they sparkled as clear as glass.

And the Latvians themselves? Ah, said the jeweller, turning away from me to open a drawer, we are connoisseurs of amber, we and the Russians. We like only rarities, such as this. He opened a large morocco leather case as he spoke. There, lying on white velvet as if the stones had been rubies, was a set of amber—necklace, ear-rings, and brooch—each piece framed in pale gold. The amber itself was a golden colour, flawed with a powdering of gold dust that sparkled when each piece was moved.

Amber like that, said the jeweller, is worth mounting in precious metal. Such pieces, too, cannot be faked. Then he showed me how to distinguish real amber from the synthetic beads which can imitate it so closely. If you rub real amber with a scrap of tissue paper, the paper will adhere to it, but will drop off the false stuff the moment you stop rubbing.

So if I came on a heap of shingle or sea-wrack, I would turn it over with my foot; but of course I never found anything. And the holiday-makers, picnicking on the dunes, would watch me idly or wave in a friendly way. But I could not hear their voices for the deep boom of the sea.

5

ABOUT a week after my arrival, the Professor returned from her holiday.

Leaving me in possession of her bedroom, she contented herself with a bed made up on the sofa of her study each night. Our household became a *ménage à trois*. She laughed heartily when I told her of the Baron's obvious discomfiture at my arrival. Thinking he would be away on holiday during my visit, she had not considered it necessary to inform him that I was coming. After her own departure, his holiday had been changed to a later date. The unexpected arrival of a strange foreign woman must have occasioned him considerable surprise.

"But what does it matter"—she gave her jolly laugh again— "since we three get on so well together?"

She was just what I had expected : grey-haired, energetic, and full of enthusiasm for the development of her country's future. Her father's official duties had led to his bringing up his family first in Petersburg and then in Kieff. She had therefore lived most of her life under the Russian Empire, in purely Russian surroundings. But under a veneer of education she still remained a Latvian peasant.

Rootless herself, she did not understand roots in others. She was curiously naïve. She had been to America, and had there absorbed the more showy facets of modern educational life. Her bookshelves were full of "Quick Ways" to this or that; her walls were strewn with pennons from small Middle Western colleges which (she insisted) had far more life in them than the older seats of learning in the East. The wisdom which comes of long experience and a settled way of life was quite inexplicable to her, because you couldn't get it out of a text-book, nor could you acquire it during a college course.

Yet, beneath this shallow veneer of civilization, one caught glimpses of her own essential peasant nature, which was sweet, true, and quickly generous. And I admired, too, the way the Baron at meals ignored her strictures upon everything he held necessary to culture and well-rooted civilization.

He merely smiled pleasantly, ate a little faster, and pushed some dish across to me. Fill your mouth as I do, his gesture seemed to say. Then you won't be tempted to waste your breath arguing. . . .

One day I asked Doctor Rauert how she, a fervent nationalist, had come to share her home with a Balt.

"It was like this," she said. "I was house-hunting and took a great fancy to this flat, but it was too big and too expensive. The last occupant had shut off the little suite opening out of the dining-room, and had let it to a lodger. I wanted to do something like that too, but could find no one ready to share expenses. I told the house agent my difficulty. He said that a Baltic nobleman had been looking at the flat and was in the same quandary. It is a pity he is a Balt, I told the agent, because of course that makes sharing out of the question. They were always aggressive and domineering, and now they will be embittered as well. No, thank you!"

"Then at that time you hadn't even met the Baron?"

"Of course not. We moved in widely different circles, both political and social. But he rang me up that night. 'Forget that I am a Balt,' he said, 'and remember only that I am a reasonable man who has suffered much and learned a little since the Revolution.' So I agreed, and he shares the rent, and Olga's wage, and keeps to his own two rooms, as I do, except at meals. He is quite tactful, too. He never talks politics, as you may have noticed."

He did not do so, certainly, while the Professor was still at table. But often she hurried out before we had had our coffee; for she bustled about a thousand occupations, even though the university, where she taught, was shut down for the summer. Then the Baron took pleasure in over turning any hopes regarding the future of Latvia which she might have raised in me by her conversation.

"All this talk about a national culture is so absurd!" he would remark conversationally, helping himself to some fruit. "Latvia never had any culture beyond what she got from us German Balts. Since the year 1200, she has been under foreign domination; first ours, then that of the Poles, the Swedes, and the Russians. Our cultural influence remained throughout all the changes of mastership. And for a people of only two million souls to talk of 'reviving' what they never had since the thirteenth century is simply ridiculous!"

"At least they kept hold of their language," I suggested.

"What good is a primitive language to a nation of only two million, when it has the German Reich at its doors? Such half-forgotten tongues are as foolish and useless in this modern world as Erse is to the people of Ireland. One really must apply common sense to nationalism, as well as to everything else."

"Then you would like the Latvians—and perhaps the other two Baltic states as well—to speak German instead of their national languages?" I teased him. As with most Germans, he did not take teasing well.

"Say language, not languages, please," he said sharply. "It really makes me sick to hear Latvians differentiating themselves from Lithuanians and Estonians! The Estonians have perhaps some claim to a separate tongue—it has a different root from the two others—but they are all three descended from the same primitive tribe, and the little difference of language (on which they lay such stress) is no wider than the difference between Gaelic and Erse. Not that it matters," he went on more conversationally, "because in another generation or two this false, synthetic flicker of a non-existent nationalism will have died out for ever."

"Why do you say so?"

"Well"—he shrugged—"think of their united population! Hardly as many millions as I have fingers. And if you want any further reason, take a look at the map."

The remark was figurative, but made so earnestly that I found myself turning my head to stare at the empty wall where no map hung. Instead, the Baron's fine old French clock caught my eye. I jumped up. Doctor Rauert told me to meet her at the station in half an hour. We were going into the country to spend a night there with Emilia, the young dressmaker who made her clothes and had just made a summer dress for me.

Emilia was the daughter of a small farmer in the Province of Courland. She was now at home, on her yearly holiday, to help her father get in the crops. But last week we had found her still in Riga, in her lodging of one room up a rickety wooden staircase in one of the old shuttered houses down by the River Daugava, that great waterway which the Russians called the Dvina, and which had been once the chief artery for the timber export of the whole Empire.

Even so, Emilia did not occupy her room alone. She shared it with another girl from the country who worked in Schultz's Restaurant. The day we had climbed the stairs, Doctor Rauert had strolled boldly into Emilia's room without knocking, in true peasant fashion, but the room had been empty. Some pins on the floor and a length of cut-out material trailing down from the sewing-machine told us that she had only left it temporarily. While we stood there, in the middle of Emilia's floor, sounds came from the room below. I listened. It was an old, cracked gramophone playing a bit of "Swan Lake."

"Of course!" the Professor had said. "This must be Emilia's practice evening. She is a devotee of ballet, like everyone here. There is a retired ballet-mistress living down below, and the girls take a weekly class from her."

The *corps de ballet* at the Riga Opera House was famous along the shores of the Baltic, where Russian traditions still lingered. As we descended towards the music, Doctor Rauert told me impressively that the ballet mistress had once been a prima ballerina of the Maryinsky Theatre in Petersburg. Tossed up in Riga like jetsam, her day over, her savings vanished in the cataclysm of revolution, she made a living by the tuition of such as Emilia, who wished to keep fit and practise toe-dancing.

The music grew louder with every step. Through it now we could hear an old, harsh voice counting in Russian. *Ras, Dwa, Tri. . . .* The room we looked into was even barer than Emilia's.

What furniture it had was all crowded against one wall to expose the chalked floor and the practice-bar at the other end of the room. A row of girls in shabby practice tunics were going through their steps, eyes fixed anxiously upon the ageing woman who faced them. Her features were sharpened to knife-edge, her arms were muscled in whip-cord. Yet the gestures, the turn of the head, conveyed an elegance which those lumpy, perspiring girls would never reach.

Emilia had broken away and escorted us back to her room. And all the while, as she measured me, the gramophone downstairs ground out its faded tune, while the voice kept counting, *Ras, Dwa, Tri.* . . .

Today we were in the train, going to visit Emilia on her native heath. We had soon left the outskirts of Riga, and were traversing the lonely, beautiful countryside. This, the Province of Courland, was the early background of the peasant girl who became first the mistress and then the wife of Peter the Great. From one of these primitive huts had emerged the woman who became Catherine the First, ruling Russia in her own right after her husband's death.

Latvia has a thousand lakes. The flat forest lands alternated with them, so that the train seemed to be circling a succession of round plates painted blue by the sky above and bordered with a pattern of silver birches. Everything looked still as in a mirror. Now and then the railway-track ran sinuously along some narrow isthmus of land between two tracts of water, and I would lean forward to watch the miracle of the water appearing to fill the windows on both sides of the carriage at once, with no land apparent from where we sat.

There were three people in the carriage besides ourselves. One looked like a servant-girl going to her first place in some farm in the depths of the country. She sat with her red scrubbed hands on her knees, and her luggage—a coffin-shaped case made of polished pine bark—above her head on the rack. The others were a small business-man and his wife. Both were dressed in their best and looked perfectly square, as though cut out of wood. They kept themselves to themselves, but their eyes were fixed beadily upon the Professor and me, because we were talking English.

The train kept threading woods and water alternately like a great black darning-needle. The business-man's wife began to unpack a parcel of sandwiches and handed them round. We all bit into slabs of rye bread and cheese, and the ice was broken. The servant-girl confided the name of the place to which she was going. And I looked out of the window again, because now they were all talking in Latvian together, on account of the girl, instead of the German the couple had used for my benefit.

There were saw-mills now, all along the route, and clanking rafts of logs travelling down the rivers. Once I caught sight of a band of gypsies driving two or three poor-looking horses before them over a bridge. "Probably stolen," Doctor Rauert said to me, "as were most of the horses you saw for sale in the market. Gypsies are adept at treating them so that they show to advantage—for an hour or two. Stolen horses are the chief stock-in-trade of the Courland gypsies. If one is lame, they doctor it so that it becomes nervous and fidgety, and its movements suggest high spirits as well as masking the lameness."

They looked poor enough creatures, the horses crossing the bridge. Head down, they trotted clumsily on legs thick as bedposts. Anything less like high spirits I could not imagine, and said so. But Doctor Rauert, who had been peering through the glass at them with a professional eye, told me they were "useful enough." She added that she knew about horses, having bought them for a Cossack regiment during the war. That had been her war service; travelling from one horse-market to the next, choosing mounts.

"I always loved and understood horses," she said, "and, as you know, women were conscripted to serve in all sorts of ways during the war. That was my job. Let me tell you one thing, dear Elisabeth. The highly bred English bloodstock I see winning races in the cinema news-reel, the fine hunters and so on, they would be useless in a campaign! No, a good cavalry horse is one bred to hard work, accustomed to hard living, even to shortage of food, for then it knows how to endure. It is not

speed or grace, but endurance, that is wanted in Cossack war-
fare!"

The train was slowing down. The servant-girl stretched up
and fetched her wooden case off the rack. We bade her good-
bye as she climbed down on to what looked like a mere sandy
track. Close to the track, however, there stood a large house,
gleaming with new white paint. It was evidently of some consequence, having a broad, pillared terrace which commanded a
view of the distant village (looking like a lot of creosoted packing cases), and the sapphire-coloured lake beyond.

"That used to be the castle of Count ——" Doctor Rauert
told me, "and the girl has been engaged to work there. It is now
a sanatorium, you know. High time that it served some useful
purpose!"

She spoke with distinct venom. I suggested, to tease her, that
she seemed to dislike the old Baltic landowners even more than
the Russians.

"Well, of course! What do you think? So long as we slaved
for them as serfs, they were kind enough; but let one of us try to
raise our head, try to get a little education, and p'ff! we were
knocked down in the mud again."

The woman sitting opposite seemed to grasp what we had
been saying. In any case, she had seen me crane my neck to
catch a last glimpse of the lonely great house as it slipped behind
us. She began to pour forth words in Latvian, gesticulating,
making signs that my companion would translate. I would not
have believed she could be so animated.

"She says that her mother once acted as foster-mother to the
wife of one of those Balts. For you must know, it was not the
custom for the highly-born to nurse their own children. No,
they would choose a strong, healthy woman, who must live at
the castle for nine months, getting the best of everything certainly, but forbidden to set foot in her home or see her own husband or baby during all that time, for fear she carried some
infection back to the castle. But the neighbour in charge of her
mother's first child neglected it, and it died. Think of that poor
woman's homecoming!"

The wooden pair opposite were staring at me, trying to guess the impact of the English words through my expression. Then the man spoke, and Doctor Rauert again translated. "He says an aunt of his father's was once foster-mother, in the days before flogging had died out. She could not bear the separation from her own child. She stole down to the village and played a little with her baby. But the German steward caught her on her way back. She got twenty lashes, there in the courtyard, with her shoulders bared before everyone."

She rose as she spoke, for the train was slowing down. The late afternoon sun now bathed the fields about us with gold. A little wood of silver birches shaded the wooden station shed, and as we got down on the line, Emilia stepped out from the trees and came towards us.

6

"Welcome!" she smiled, and, drawing her bare brown feet together, made a little bow. Then she took our suitcases from us and led the way back through the wood, towards the fields on the other side. There, in a hollow, I saw two buildings. One was a round thatched hut with a hole in the thatch which, in long-ago winters, had let out the smoke from the fire burning in the middle of the floor. Here Emilia's grandparents had lived, in the old, bad days. Now it was used as a shelter for cattle.

Emilia's home lay a little way off. It was built of wood and not very much larger, but she was proud of it. There was only one single, large room besides the kitchen, and a little chamber in which she, being a wage-earner and a sophisticated towns-woman, kept her own possessions and ornaments. This room she offered to me.

In the large room the family ate by day and slept by night. There were wide benches running round all four walls, which served them as beds. When I asked the Professor where she would sleep, she laughed and said she would mark out her length on the bench with the others. Just now, however, a table in the middle of the room had been spread with a brightly embroidered cloth, and set with pottery bowls and big iron spoons.

Emilia's mother came in from the kitchen and greeted us. She carried an iron pan, full of roasted beans, and began doling them into the bowls. A plate of pale butter, churned by Emilia herself, was now placed in the middle of the table. One helped oneself to a lump of butter, which melted in rivulets down the pile of roasted beans in one's bowl, and then washed down the supper with a glass of milk.

By this time the room had grown almost dark. The eyes of Emilia's little brother were round with sleep. From time to time the rest of the family yawned loudly, having been up and working since dawn. While the mother cleared the crockery off the table, Emilia opened a chest, pulled out a bundle of sheepskins and blankets, and disposed them about the hard benches round the room. And then I got a fright. For something moved, high up near the rafters, in the darkest corner of the room.

An old, old woman had stirred herself from what I had thought was a mass of rags piled on top of the unlit stove. The stove itself was a great brick erection, square-topped, with an oven door. And the old woman had been lying on top of it, asleep.

"She is Emilia's grandmother," whispered the Professor in my ear. "What a job they had to get her to move to her son's nice new house! She did not want to leave the thatched hut, where all her children had been born; but it was unseemly for her to remain in such a primitive dwelling, now he is a freeman, with his own farm. At least she likes his stove. It keeps her so beautifully warm in winter, she stays up there all the time."

The old woman must have slept through the meal. Now she hung over the rim of the stove, her clawlike hands grasping the bricks, staring at me. I was glad to escape from that steady stare to my own little room. There, on Emilia's straw mattress, I slept uneasily, because there was only a wooden partition between myself and the others, and her father snored loudly all night.

As soon as the dawn turned my one little window pink, I heard them groaning and stirring. Presently Doctor Rauert passed the window, carrying a tin jug in one hand, with a white towel over her arm. Then Emilia came in with a mug of hot coffee, and a basin and jug of cold water for me to wash with. But long before I had dressed, everyone else had gone out, and the big room was silent again.

I stepped out of doors and looked around. The whole landscape was bathed in that clear, greenish light of early morning. The house faced east, and the clear hard light, untouched as yet by warmth, shone on the grey clapboards and glittered on the nails in the horseshoes fastened above the door for luck. Down the slope, from the direction of the little wood, came Doctor Rauert, singing and waving her towel in the air to dry it as she walked.

"I bathed in the little stream down there!" she exclaimed. "The birches made a screen for me, and how delicious it was to feel the fresh air about me and the cold water stream over my shoulders as I poured it out of my jug!"

Her return to nature was perfectly genuine. There was no affectation about it at all. Here, in this countryside, in the primitive simplicity of Emilia's home, she had completely shed the rather rudimentary sophistication bestowed by her duties at the university and her visit to America. Here she was happy and at home.

"Emilia is just coming," she went on. "She has gone to drive the geese into the fields before we start."

I could hear the geese honking. Presently they lurched round the corner of the farm, making in single file for the field at the side. And after them came Emilia, but transformed even from the girl I had seen last night. She was wearing her gala costume in honour of the fair. Over her brilliant dress hung a white, homespun cloak gathered at one shoulder by an enormous silver brooch. And she was wearing a silver crown; a circlet of balls on spikes which gave her enormous dignity. Every family in the Province owned such a crown, to be worn by the eldest un-married daughter on high days and holidays. The polishing of her crown had been the work of yesterday for Emilia.

Her father brought round the long market cart in which we were to travel. It seemed to sag in the middle, and we sat on the floor which, though strewn with a thin cushion of hay, was still very hard. Emilia sat on what one might call the prow of the cart, in order to drive the horse. And the horse was lazy, mean-dering through the fields or trotting for a minute or two in response to the whip, before going back to its meditative walk.

Emilia cracked her whip again and then sighed. "We shall never get there!"

It was then the Professor showed me that she did indeed

know how to manage horses. "Change places with me," she ordered, "and give me the reins."

With a sigh of relief, Emilia subsided into the bottom of the cart. Already she had told us that horses were not her affair; it was always her father who looked after and drove them. The minute the reins passed into Doctor Rauert's capable hands, the horse stopped his nonsense. She did not once use the whip. But a current of authority seemed to travel down from her hands to the bit. We had no more trouble at all.

Now, on the horizon there showed the dark line of a village. It seemed far enough away, but the air was so clear, one could see the purplish line of smoke hanging above it, made by the fires in each house. "Listen!" said the Professor, pulling up for a moment. We listened. Though we could see neither dancers nor band, we heard the faint musical throbbing.

"They hold the fair in the fields on the other side of the village," Emilia explained.

The Professor was just going to shake the reins and start the horse forward again, but Emilia pointed to one of the tiny, innumerable lakes or ponds lying like saucers in the hollows of the fields.

"I want to look at my reflection," she said. "I have the feeling that my crown is not straight."

We all got out of the cart to look at our reflections, because, after all, the drive had been long and dusty, and we would shortly be on view. Emilia went down on her knees on the grass verge. Her white cloak flowed out on either side of her. We stooped down and looked over her shoulder. The air was quite still and the water as clear as glass. We could see our faces distinctly, above the spikes of Emilia's crown. We could watch her reflection curve its arms upwards to adjust the crown, one hand drawing out a long silver pin, then shoving it in again more securely.

Then we went back to the cart. The horse seemed to have heard the music too, for it jerked its head up smartly and almost galloped towards the village, flinging Emilia and me together and jolting us in a most painful manner. Now the tune reached us distinctly, and soon, as we drove in a curve round the village itself, we could see the booths and the flags, and the coloured movement of crowds milling about the stalls. We could see the cleared space for the dancers in the middle of the field. The women had all discarded their white cloaks, which lay like snowdrifts where they were dropped on the stubble. As they danced, their brilliantly embroidered skirts made a moving pattern of colour beneath the blazing sun.

But the sun began to go down at last. The band stopped, and horses were put between the shafts again. Those who had come from far off, like ourselves, wanted to reach their homes before dark. I watched the carts move off in all directions, across the reaped fields where the long shadows lay. But there was still enough light to glint on the silver crowns of the women, seated majestically with their white cloaks now gathered around them against the cool of the evening. And I wondered whether the Courland peasant girl, Catherine, had been wearing her crown when Peter the Great first saw her and decided that she was fit to wear an imperial one.

7

THERE was one shop in the Smitsu Iela which always held me entranced. It was an antique shop, and most of its goods were Russian. Besides the peasant lacquer work in gold and red and the strings of Baltic amber it had for sale, it also displayed things of much more value. Here were ikons, specimens of old Russian enamel work, barbaric silver, and jewellery. But mostly ikons.

I was staring at one when I felt a touch on my arm. I looked round, thinking it would be one of the usual Black Market touts who haunted the vicinity of the Bourse. But it was the Baron.

"Is this interest in Byzantine art by any chance genuine?" he asked, smiling. "Or were you merely trying to get a better exchange for your English pounds?"

I told him I was genuinely interested in the ikons. "I, too, love ikons," he said, beginning to walk down the street beside me. "But the best are difficult to come by now. At first there were plenty to be bought in Riga. White Russian refugees sold them just after the Revolution, so as to have money to live on. I have heard a rumour, however, that a branch of the Old Believers still exists here, and that they have some very fine and ancient ikons brought out of Russia at the time of Peter the Great."

I asked who the Old Believers were.

"They were the last-ditchers, as you might call them. The members of the Orthodox Church who stood out against the Church reforms of Peter the Great. He had several liturgical errors corrected; purged the ritual of later additions, and changed the language of the Mass from the ancient Slavonic, which few people understood any more, to modern Russian. He persecuted those who refused to conform, so that many of them fled to other countries to form new colonies. One such colony still lives on the shores of the Black Sea, where they call themselves Lipovani, I believe."

I supposed that the Old Believers must have brought their valuable ikons with them, when they came to live on the fringe of Peter's Empire to be as far away from him as possible. The Baron agreed, adding that he had heard how fine examples had been smuggled out to them afterwards for safe keeping, by wealthy sympathizers too deeply involved in Russian politics or commerce to want to sacrifice themselves by joining the Brethren openly.

Considering his fondness of the arts, it seemed odd that the Baron knew so little about this rare collection. It sounded as if he had not even bothered to try to see it. I hinted my surprise. It was not often that I saw him at a loss, but he gave me a helpless, sideways glance, then quickened his steps as if trying to escape from something he could not explain.

"It seems absurd," he said at last, "but really, I and my German friends have always kept rather aloof from the Russians and their interests here. It is a long time since I heard anyone mention the Old Believers at all. Perhaps the sect has died out and their treasures have been already dispersed. Who knows? In any case, they were very secretive, allowing no one to pry into their affairs and their possessions unless vouched for by one of themselves. Or it may only have been a rumour that they had any treasures at all!"

But he said it half-heartedly, obviously believing in the old tale. So I said I would ask Doctor Rauert. At that he smiled again. "Don't count on her helping you even if she could! Latvians only wish to forget the old Russian days as quickly as possible."

He was right there at least. The Professor showed astonishment and scorn at my interest. She knew nothing about the ikon collection, and cared less. "Just dirty old bits of painted wood, that's all they'll be." She sniffed. "And as for the Old Believers —a more ignorant, squalid set one can hardly imagine. At least that's what they used to be like. Whether they still exist somewhere along the Moscow Road is a thing I can't tell you."

The Moscow Road. She never could understand why that long road fascinated me so. She was ashamed of it, for it was the only part of Riga still stamped with the hall-mark of Russia. It began at the farther end of the market-hall, where a mosaic ikon under a stone canopy stood as frontier outpost. It meandered along the bank of the River Dougava, growing shabbier at every step. Once its proximity to the river had made it an important district of the city. Now that Riga's export shipping had dwindled, it had decayed, until only the poorer of its Russian population stayed on, together with one or two conservative merchants who still refused to leave their old homes.

Ramshackle tea-houses lined its length. In between them, the carved wooden frontages of houses belonging to Jewish or Armenian merchants bulged forward or stood awry. Many of those houses stood empty now, vacated by their former owners and given over to the gypsies who lived here in winter, or to the poorest class of Russians who herded together converting them into rabbit warrens.

Once I had delayed in the market-hall until the closing hour, and then had wandered a little way up the Moscow Road as the quick dusk was falling. One by one the lights of the tea-houses sprang out invitingly, until they made a ribbon of orange beads marking the length of the river. The crumbling wooden houses all had verandahs. Bands of gypsies on their way home from the market were squatting on the steps of some of them. They sat on their bundles, chattering or playing cards; glancing up now and then at the sound of horses' hooves, as one of their number rode by on a piece of unsaleable merchandise.

The crazy shutters of the tea-houses gaped sufficiently for me to catch glimpses of their interiors as I passed. I could see little groups of Russian peasants sitting about bare tables, each with a glass of amber-coloured tea before him. At their elbows were jugs of hot water, ordered at the same time as the tea so as to avoid the expense of paying for a second glass. Now and then an arm would lift, dribbling some hot water into the glass, for as long as liquid of some sort stood on the table before him, the shabby, weary customer could not be ejected. And from Riga to even the nearest Russian village was a long drive. . . .

The Professor had said that the Old Believers and their treasure were to be found somewhere down the Moscow Road. It was the likeliest place for them, but who would be willing to take me there?

Suddenly I remembered Michael. He was a young man whom Doctor Rauert had come across during her epic visit to America. The son of Latvian emigrants who had made good in the States, he had turned up unexpectedly at the flat and had called several times since. He wore very pale suits, very wide hats and a gentle, ingratiating expression. He had taken me to see the great Orthodox cathedral, and in front of one of the ikons had explained that what he called "the lady" was called Mary and was Our Lord's mother. I smiled at the recollection. Of course Michael was Orthodox himself, and he probably thought that since I was not I must be a heathen.

Being Orthodox must mean being Russian. Doctor Rauert had evidently made an exception in Michael's favour. To make sure, I asked him next time I saw him. Yes, he said, his father had been Russian, a clerk in one of the timber-yards. Did he, by any chance, know any of the Old Believers? He shook his head and reminded me that he had been born in the States. But when I mentioned the Moscow Road he brightened. For the yard where his father had worked had been down the Moscow Road, and he knew an Armenian merchant, a friend of his father's, who lived there still.

"I will inquire," he told me kindly.

The next time I saw him he had good news. The merchant would take us to see the ikons hanging in the Old Believers' chapel, for he knew where it was and was well acquainted with the sect. Apparently they ran a little hospital and school for their own people, but were always short of funds. And the Armenian (who dealt in antiques as well as other things) occasionally bought from them some family ikon, piece of enamel work, or jewellery bequeathed by a follower who had nothing else to leave.

One would never guess, from the outside of the crazy wooden house, that its owner was a wealthy man. It and the houses on each side of it bore the same peeled and blistered paint, the same slanting window-frames looking as if they would at any minute fall out into the street. But Michael told me that was intentional. It is never wise, he said, to be ostentatious about wealth in places like the Moscow Road.

There was a bell-pull hanging from a chain just under the hooded porch. We could hear its cracked note reverberating through the house. Presently the door opened, and we were invited to enter an enormous room at the farther end of a passage so dark that I kept bumping into corners of the furniture before we got there.

Ruby-coloured velvet curtains were drawn half-way across windows looking on to a yard and then to the river below. Ornate gilded mirrors hung opposite them, reflecting a glimpse of the squalor outside. The furniture was mostly French, and a clutter of valuable but slightly dirty silver ornaments lay about on little tables, interspersed with jewelled Easter eggs by Fabergé and old snuff-boxes. A lean and half-starved cat crouched on a window-sill, peering in angrily. I could hear, from far away, on the other side of the glass, the faint hoot of a tug going down the river.

While I was staring at all this, the Armenian merchant had risen from a corner of the room and was coming forward to greet us. He bowed obsequiously in my direction, then shook Michael by the hand. "I am happy to be of service to your English friend," he remarked politely in French; adding, "indeed, without me I doubt if the Old Believers would permit her to view their treasures. They are, alas! apt to be suspicious with strangers."

"But they trust you," said Michael.

"Well, they come to me when in need of money," the merchant said, edging us towards the door. "And I either advance the sum needed, or buy what they have to sell. I dare say that gives them confidence."

He smiled into his beard and opened the door. We stepped

out of the house, into the long winding road. Between the houses, each as decayed and apparently abandoned as the one we had left, the black water of the Dougava showed, where it passed the bottom of fenced rubbish heaps which had once been gardens.

Half-way along the road the merchant stopped. "Just five minutes' delay," he appeared to beg us, "while I have a word with the ikon-mender here."

The big houses with their yards were now giving way to small shops. Nearly all had cellars, the tops of whose windows rose in crescent half-moons above the pavement, and the cellars, too, had been let out as shops. The ikon-mender's little work-shop was a vault half-sunk beneath the level of the road. His shutters were open to let in the air and light.

We stooped to peer through them. Their tops, curved out-ward, just came to our waists. I saw someone bending over a panel of painted wood which lay on the bench in the middle of the room. He was dabbing at it tenderly with a piece of rag. Saucers full of colours already mixed lay around on the bench. One of them, catching the shaft of light from the street, seemed to be full of gold dust. The light played over the opposite wall, showing stacks of canvases, empty gilt frames, and more painted panels propped up on the floor. Above them hung a row of cheap, gaudy pictures of Orthodox saints. These were evidently for sale.

The Armenian called down into the room. The ikon-mender looked up. He was an enormous man, heavily bearded, and his hands were so large it seemed incredible that they could work as delicately as they did. He lumbered over to the window, grasping the tops of the shutters as he talked to the Armenian. They spoke in Russian, and Michael tried to follow, his eyes strained under the big pale Stetson hat. One could see the Russian and the American clashing inside him as he tried to recall the few words of Russian picked up when he was a child.

Then the ikon-mender went back to his bench, and we walked on. The Armenian was full of flowing apologies for his incivility in speaking a foreign language before me. He explained that he had been giving instructions about the restoration of an ikon just bought from the Brothers. It had belonged to one of the inmates of their home for the aged and destitute, and had been left to them by the lonely creature after his death.

"It is shockingly darkened by lamp smoke," he told us, "but that can be removed, with care and skill. The colour is good, and where it is not so good, my friend back yonder can improve it a little. I dare say I shall get a good price for it on the Smitsu Iela."

We were now entering a narrow lane. At its farther end stood a group of buildings, faintly Byzantine in outline. Those were the chapel, the hospital, and the schools belonging to the Old Believers. At the chapel door the merchant hesitated.

"I dare not go in with you," he said sadly. "The ikons here always make my mouth water too much."

But he came, all the same. The chapel itself was a bare place, divided down the middle by a row of pillars forming a centre aisle. I had never seen such a thing in an Orthodox church, but the Armenian explained that here the men stood on one side of the chapel and the women on the other, according to the old habit before the innovations of Peter the Great.

"And look!" He pointed. "See, they use only candles! That is not poverty alone, it is a protest against the introduction of gas or electricity."

Bare though the place might be, its walls were clothed and painted by its priceless collection of ikons. They hung, three and four deep, glowing with colour. Here were none of the later examples which look so much more valuable to the novice; the ones plated with silver or gold cut out to show only the painted heads and hands which mark the decline of ikonography. Almost all which hung round the walls of the chapel were of the sixteenth and seventeenth centuries.

The Armenian merchant sighed as he looked at them. "The Old Believers left Russia before the decline in ikon-painting became too widespread. Therefore, the specimens they brought with them from their churches, or from the hands of wealthy sympathizers, were the finest obtainable."

"I guess they can't sell them because they're church property," Michael put in, touching my arm as he spoke.

"That is so," said the merchant. He sighed again.

We left the chapel and entered the home which looked after poor old people belonging to the community. Here the Armenian lingered, talking to the lay brother at the gate. Michael and I hesitated, but the merchant, interrupting his conversation for a moment, waved us on.

"I told them you were coming. It's all right. Nobody will stop you if you walk around."

The smell of poverty grew stronger as we reached the wards. The old men, lean as vultures, looked up dully as we walked through their dormitory. Some were already roosting on the edge of their beds, tearing with their broken teeth at the hunks of black bread handed round to them by a young monk with a straggling red beard. I thought Michael looked rather pale when we stepped into the corridor again.

"If my parents had not gone to America," he said, "I might some day have been visiting them here...."

There was more life and bustle in the big room given over to the old women. Several of them were busy cooking their own suppers of potatoes or cabbage soup. They cooked in battered cans arranged on top of a great charcoal stove, bending over the cans like witches to poke whatever was inside with an iron spoon.

This part of the room seemed common ground; but the farther end of it was divided into cubicles, and as nobody seemed to be in them just now, I wandered towards them to see what they were like. Each had a bed and a small table on which stood a pitcher and ewer for washing. And yet each was entirely different. Its owner had invariably managed to hold on to some treasure salved from the wreck of her fortunes. One had a dim, painted chest of drawers with her initials and a date embellishing the top; another had clung to a wooden chair carved in the style of peasant baroque; and all had managed to dispose of faded photographs or crude holy pictures so as to create around them a faint aura of their own lost personality.

Somebody touched my arm. It was an old nun with a stupid, vacant face. She muttered something in Russian, and Michael managed to translate. "She is inviting you to visit the old woman over there—the one in her bed. She says she has lain there for years, cared for by the Order, just like a cabbage, she says. Will you go?"

I had thought all the cubicles were empty. I did not want to go forward in the least. But the nun pulled at my skirt, as if offering a rare treat, and I could do nothing less than follow her. She was right, the figure in the bed showed no more consciousness than a cabbage. Her eyes were half-open but saw nothing. Her mouth was half-open too, and it seemed to snore. The nun patted the hump under the bedclothes as if she was proud of it, and said something to me in Russian, in a loud, harsh voice.

Michael had followed us and was standing behind me. "She says she will die quite soon," he translated.

I turned my head sharply away. I was looking now at the one solid wall of the cubicle. A set of shelves hung on it. They were clumsily lined with red plush and edged with dirty lace. Along them stood one or two trifles, a faded photograph or two, and several of those little brass triptychs, showing the Crucifixion in relief against a blue enamel background, which the godly suspend by cord around their necks. Above the shelves was an ikon showing St George slaying the dragon. It was a good ikon, glowing with colour.

"The nun is saying that they like to have their little possessions about them," Michael translated again, in a dull flat voice.

Down at the farther end of the room there was still bustle and life. The other old women could still move about, could savour what they were cooking, and quarrel and snap at each other for getting in the way of the communal dish of salt. But the one in the bed beside us would take no more interest in anything now. She had finished with cooking and such things for ever.

Gradually the sensation of being rooted to the spot wore off.

I was able to turn my back on the bed and walk back towards the other old women. Michael looked pale and thoughtful. He knew what I was thinking, too, for he touched my sleeve and said gently, "Don't forget, she's being as well looked after as they know how. The blankets were quite clean, I noticed that particularly. And she has been allowed to keep all that stuff on the shelves——"

"The ikon was a good one," I said.

"Yes, it was."

We passed the big stove with its iron top and the battered tins smoking with food. Now we were in the entrance hall again, where the Armenian still stood gesticulating, talking to one of the Brothers.

Michael dropped his voice and said hurriedly, "Don't let's talk any more about the ikon." I knew what he meant, and nodded. However illogical and stupid the thought was, I had it too.

Outside, the dusk had fallen already. Our footsteps clattered down the lane, then were drowned, on entering the Moscow Road, by the laughter and shouts from a tea-house opposite. Although it was still late summer, a cold wind blew off the Dougava, whipping us each time we passed by a gap between the houses which stood with their backs to the river.

The ikon-mender had put up his shutters against the damp. One could see the thin line of gold lamplight showing where they met. When we got out of the Moscow Road at last, the brilliant electric haze from the street lamps and shops in the modern part of the city almost blinded us; for our eyes had got used to the softness of oil-lamps and the mole-grey of where we had come from.

Even the Baron had felt chilly that night, I remember, because it was the only night he had lit the elegant porcelain stove in his own little sitting-room. Or perhaps he had lit it in my honour, because I was leaving next morning. He swung back its little brass doors to let me see the firewood crackling behind them. And he served Doctor Rauert and me with coffee in his best Dresden-china cups.

He would have listened with interest as well as politeness, to my story of what I had seen down the Moscow Road. But Doctor Rauert could not see that a slum could afford any interest; much less a Russian slum. She moved her coffee-cup irritatedly here and there over the marble surface of the Empire table, as if it were a pawn. And the Baron, nervous about his china, soon switched the conversation to something else.

Part Three

THE FALLEN MINARET

8

BECAUSE Berlin was so much farther South and inland, it was much warmer. The tail-end of summer had been arrested here, although there seemed a good deal of dust and exhaustion about. Frau Schmolke looked a little tired and pasty, I thought, when she knocked at my door and came in to greet me on my return to the Pension Schmolke.

"And how did it go in Riga?"

She nodded her massive head as she listened. Then she gave me her own news. The nice American couple were on holiday still, in the Black Forest. Nicolai had almost lost his voice singing out of doors in a garden restaurant all summer, but with luck and care would regain it in time to tackle his winter engagements. The rest were as usual, except for Paul, who was being difficult.

Paul, the brilliant young Hungarian pianist, was Frau Schmolke's special protégé. She said his temperament made life more difficult for him than it was for the others. When the others reminded her heatedly that they had temperaments too, she would point out that Paul was thinner than any of them, which meant that his temperament wore him out more.

So I was surprised to hear her admit that he could be difficult. It all arose from the fact that during high summer, when so many of her regular boarders were on holiday, Frau Schmolke was obliged to open her doors to ordinary tourists. Ordinary tourists did not appreciate the constant practising indulged in by the few musicians who, like Paul and Nicolai, had summer engagements which kept them in Berlin still.

"In the mornings it did not matter," Frau Schmolke told me, "because the tourists went out immediately after breakfast. So nobody was disturbed. But those who were *en pension* with me, naturally returned to take lunch. And after lunch they wished to repose. I had therefore to make a new rule, and you know, Liebe Fräulein, how distasteful rules are to everyone here! I said, Let there be no practising between the hours of two and five."

"How did the others take it?" I asked with interest. Frau Schmolke eased her weight on to the end of my olive-green sofa.

"Quite well, considering," she told me. "Of course, I had explained that the rule was temporary, and would be thrown overboard with the tourists just as soon as I could fill my rooms again. Only Paul did not see its necessity. I do not myself remember his ever wishing to practise in the afternoon before. But now he says that no other time of day suits him so well."

"I shouldn't listen to him, he's only trying it on. . . ."

But she put out a plump white hand to stop the cruel words. "It is his temperament, he cannot help it. Look how thin he is! Good, fattening food I give him, but the flame inside him burns it all up before it can settle on his bones."

"Well?" I asked. Paul was an excellent pianist, but I didn't believe for a moment that he had more flames inside him than Nicolai, for example.

Then Frau Schmolke showed her quality, and the essential judgment and fairness which had given the Pension Schmolke its unique position in Berlin life. "I could not allow him to practise and not the others." She said. "So, when he said he would go rather than obey, I said Go."

I looked at her with respect. Paul had been like a son, or a favourite grandson, to this childless widow. Moreover, he had been under her roof a whole year. "Where has he gone?" I asked.

Unexpectedly, she gave her large, soft smile. "Only to the *pension* farther up the Nürnbergerstrasse! I sometimes send ordinary tourists there when I have no room and am sorry for them. He will not be so comfortable, poor boy! But it won't be for long."

"So you will let him come back when the tourists go?"

She gave a fat chuckle. "Either then, or when he gives his

autumn recital, whichever happens first. Who else but myself can tie a white tie so that it is an honour to the platform?"

I smelt the breakfast coffee next morning as I walked down the long corridor to the Speisezimmer. There was the tang of furniture polish in it too, because a little maid was polishing the hall on hands and knees, and she turned round so quickly to wish me good-morning that her newly pinned-up plaits fell down of their own weight, making her look like a schoolgirl again.

Unlike most *pensions*, the Pension Schmolke did not encourage morning coffee in one's room. The long table down the middle of the Speisezimmer was strewn with baskets of rolls and saucers of butter and jam. Almost immediately one sat down the second of the two little maids who did all the work would appear with one's cup of coffee. That was all.

And, as it was late, most of the other guests seemed to have finished theirs already. Only two people remained in the room. One was Nicolai, eating his breakfast collarless, with what looked like a cold compress about his throat. The other was the lady whom Frau Schmolke had already told me of, a few minutes before, calling her scornfully "Die Lorelei."

"My fault it was, for accepting her without knowing anything about her," she had said, "but with tourists, how can one tell? Musicians are different; one can always obtain some idea from the others."

"What is the matter with her?"

But Frau Schmolke would not say, or at best would only hint darkly. "I did not see her myself the night she arrived. But I went into her room to make down her bed, and no decent woman has underclothes like that one. One look at the pompons on her bedroom slippers was sufficient to tell me all."

I had entered the room rather suddenly, but Nicolai gave the impression of having backed his chair steadily away from the stranger until he was now pressed against the wall. Die Lorelei, a woman of uncertain age, was leaning across the table yearningly. Her hair was very yellow and her eyes very made up. I could see what Frau Schmolke meant. There was an aura of Edwardian voluptuousness about her which suggested pompons at once.

Nicolai looked overjoyed to see me. "Dear Elisabeth, how delightful! Excuse me that I save my voice for tonight; singing in those outdoor restaurants is the devil."

"The poor boy is practically speechless!" Lorelei spoke excellent English with a slight Cockney accent. Memories of all I had read about the Empire Promenade came sharply into my mind.

Nicolai vanished. Lorelei lit a cigarette. "What a stuffy place this is! Have you been here before? But yes, of course, you and the Russian seem to know one another. . . . I am staying here almost by accident. Really, it was most funny. I arrived in Berlin a week ago, and went, of course, to the Adlon, thinking a friend of mine would be there. But he wasn't, and I could not contemplate staying there myself, I would be far too lonely. Someone had told me this place was *gemütlich*, but it is so very primitive, one could laugh! Each day I mean to set out and look for new lodgings, but I am too lazy. . . ."

She smoked with great nonchalance as she spoke, but I had had time to notice that her smart suit was worn and her frilled blouse needed laundering. She did not look exactly poor, in which case I would have been sorry for her; but she most certainly looked as though somebody else would have had to pay her bills at the Adlon. And I grew annoyed with her for being supercilious about the Pension Schmolke.

But Nemesis was at hand. Frau Schmolke herself entered the room, an open letter in her hand. Lorelei stubbed out her cigarette and switched over to German.

"Gnädige Frau, may I have another pillow for my bed? And if you could instruct the chamber-maid not to make *quite* so much noise outside my room in the early morning, I would be obliged!"

"Certainly." Frau Schmolke spoke with a blandness which I knew to be quite deceptive. I had heard her use those bland tones before. "Is there anything further the Gnädige Frau would like?"

If Lorelei had had any sense she would have stopped there. It was probably from lack of it that she had not been more successful in life. I held my breath. Sure enough, she rushed forward to her doom.

"Yes, there is one little thing, really so unimportant, I quite forgot to mention it before. Lili, my Belgian griffon, is coming in from the country tomorrow. She has been staying with friends, but now I hear the poor darling is homesick, so I wrote yesterday, telling my friends to put her in the train. She will sleep with me, of course."

"Entschuldigen!" Frau Schmolke broke in, speaking so gently, really it was like a summer breeze fanning one's cheek. "Lili will do nothing of the kind."

"But, Liebe Frau Schmolke, she will sleep nowhere else! If one left her in this room, for example, she would howl the house down——"

"She will not be left in this room. Did I omit to tell you that no animals were allowed in the *pension*?"

"You certainly did!" I could hear Lorelei breathing rather quickly. Her colour had risen. "And now that my friends have refused—that is to say, they are certainly despatching Lili to Berlin tomorrow, since the poor darling is missing me so——"

"In that case, what I have to say will come quite providentially. I received this letter, asking for a room from tomorrow. It is from an old client who had already warned me that he would be returning at the beginning of the month to spend the whole winter with us. Since it is obvious that the Gnädige Frau does not find herself comfortable——"

"I did not say that!" Lorelei's cheeks had grown pinker still. "I only asked——"

"You asked me to relax a fixed rule about dogs. You have told me that the little dog Lili must come to Berlin tomorrow. I am an animal lover myself, and I am sure that Lili, too, would be more comfortable elsewhere."

"Most certainly, and I also!" Lorelei rose with some violence. "Please make my bill out. I go now to pack."

The door banged behind her. Frau Schmolke smiled her slow smile. "Thanks to Lili, we are saved! Can you lend me a pen?"

She wrote with it on the back of the used envelope she held in her hand. Then she pinned the notice on the green baize board which, as a rule, held intimations of forthcoming concerts. It read DOGS NOT ALLOWED!!! with the usual superabundance of exclamation marks in which Germans indulge.

"That way I protect myself," she said, retreating towards the door again. "No artist of real talent will be likely to clutter up his life here with a dog, and so I can take the notice down as soon as she leaves."

The *pension* felt oddly still. Now, at this fag-end of the season everything seemed to have died down to a dusty, breathless silence. The trees in the Tiergarten drooped their yellowish leaves which very soon they would lose altogether. Yet, if one walked back to the Nürnbergerstrasse at night, after the opera, there was a decided chill in the air, and the stars looked polished and bright with frost.

The evenings that Nicolai had no engagement, we would have supper in a restaurant, either by ourselves or with Gertrud Orff and sometimes Paul, who made a habit of eating there. He did not say why, but we suspected the quality of the food in the other *pension*. Nor, of course, did we allude directly to the affairs of the Pension Schmolke. But, out of kindheartedness, we would drop a little gossip here and there; of who had been and who was coming; and of which rooms had been redecorated during the summer. It was pathetic to see how eagerly Paul gathered up the crumbs.

I told Nicolai all about Riga and the Professor's enthusiasm for her newly formed country, together with the Baron's scorn of it. He listened, then shrugged his shoulders. "Pull devil, pull baker. . . . The whole idea of nationalism is a notion of the middle-class intelligentsia. The really powerful people at the top have always been internationalists. In the Tsarist days the aristocrats of my country were equally at home in Paris, on the

Riviera, in Rome, or Venice, and they preferred to speak French rather than their own language because it made them free of the civilized world. At the other end of the scale, the peasants all over the world think only of being left to look after their own little bit of land in peace and quiet. Do you suppose the average Latvian peasant cares a snuff whether he farms under the Russian, German, or any other flag, so long as his land is his own?"

"I have heard it said," put in Gertrud Orff, "that the only cause for which men will spontaneously spring to arms without coercion is that of religion—of one kind or another."

Nicolai agreed with her. "In other words, they will spontaneously fight for the right to settle their own consciences. . . . That is, if they get the chance."

The heat of summer seemed to have drained Gertrud of much of the flamboyant heartiness she had had when she first arrived. Apparently she had gone nowhere for a holiday, but had spent her time trying to get singing engagements and fix up pupils for the winter. In this she had been unsuccessful.

"It is all because I am not a member of the National-Socialist Party," she told me, and I stared, unbelieving. Although young and inexperienced, I had learned already that people will give fantastic reasons for calamity or non-success. (There was, for example, the apparently normal professor, once encountered during a dinner-party at home, who insisted that the roots of the First World War lay in the Disestablishment of the Welsh Church.)

But Gertrud had struck me as one of the honestest people I knew. She was not in the least likely to camouflage any inadequacy under so ridiculous an excuse. Besides, I knew that the other musicians in the Pension Schmolke looked on her artistry with respect.

"At least my Nansen Passport relieves me of that necessity," said Nicolai, and I saw that he believed what Gertrud was saying.

Gertrud was speaking again, with indignant emphasis.

Thank God, she belonged to a Hamburg bürgerlich family; to a city which, from the days of the Hansa League, had always turned its face outward to the rest of the world! Stung and indignant, she let loose a piece of inside information about the running of Hamburg's affairs since the advent of National Socialism, which interested Nicolai extremely.

Apparently the Party had "suggested" various sound members for key positions in the municipal government of the city. But up to now, the influence of the old merchant families had been strong enough for Hamburg to ignore such suggestions. Or, if pressure was brought to bear, then the appointments were made but equally ignored, and the business of the city looked after by a secret Junta, which carried things on as they had always been.

And, up to a short while ago, Berlin was too dependent upon Hamburg's trade with the outside world to make an issue of the matter. "But now I fear things are changing," Gertrud sighed. "One or two of these ridiculous appointments have been upheld by the Town Council, and soon my own city, where my ancestors gave a lead to local affairs for generations, will go the way of others."

"Is that why you left it?" Nicolai leaned forward, asking gently.

She nodded, and I saw for a moment sharp tears spring into her eyes. Then she blinked and banished them defiantly. "Here, though I may be disgusted, at least I am not saddened by comparisons with other days. But I should like to know what has made the Wilhelmstrasse feel so independent of Hamburg's trade all of a sudden!"

And the answer came into my mind in the shape of a bath and a bottle of aspirins. Once more I saw the vast show-rooms of Hibaudi, where everything, even the porcelain tubs, was designed to save fuel, labour, timber, whatever might have to be imported from overseas. From now on the Hamburg Docks would only handle what the National Socialist Government allowed them to handle. Poverty and unemployment would answer any refusal to come into line.

And I remembered, too, the very voice of the young girl at Hibaudi when I tried to borrow an aspirin from her. "If we possibly can, we must do without drugs. . . ."

Nicolai shrugged his shoulders. "I see nothing for it," he said, "but a concert tour in Australia."

A curious gleam came into Gertrud's eyes. It was the gleam of the trapped animal who thinks, suddenly, that it sees a way out. Then the light died out of them again. "My voice would never stand it. It is going already. Soon I can only teach. . . ."

And Nicolai, too, looked bitter when I asked him why, having spoken so much about Australia, he did not go there? "Where would I get the money to finance such a venture? What impresario would take me in hand? No one has shown much interest up to now!"

"But you have a magnificent voice!" I protested.

"The voice of itself is not enough. One must have also an outstanding personality to rise out of the rut. I have sufficient for bass solos with a choir or for a part in an operatic company. Not more than the others, but sufficient. Nowadays, to succeed as a solo artist one must have the personality of a Chaliapin. You may not believe me, Elisabeth, but I tell you this. When I was a boy in Russia I heard sing, not a few but many, voices as fine as his. Yes, every bit as fine! But they remained unknown outside of Russia. They had not the second gift which was his."

A depression hung over our table. Up till now we had always played together, as it were, like a completely integrated trio. Now I was being left behind. The other two were reading a score which I could not even understand. I felt they would have liked to go on playing together, but I had suddenly become the audience and they did not want me to listen.

I tried to tell myself it was only because I was tired and they unduly temperamental. But that night, at supper, a thought came into my mind which had held no interest for me before.

"May I allow myself to offer you some bread, Fräulein?" The young Kapellmeister of the State Opera turned his bald head politely in my direction. He was one of the hardest workers of everyone there; a sound musician and a good-natured soul; nor had I ever heard him talk the Party clap-trap at Frau Schmolke's table.

But he held a State job. Did that mean he was a member of the Party, just the same? And if so, was it because of the job?

9

It was only a few days before I left, that Frau Schmolke suddenly remembered the message which had come for me during my absence in Riga.

"I must apologize with dust on my head! Had it seemed important, I would have immediately taken a note and left it for you to collect when you came back. But they only asked if they might speak with you, and when I said No, you were no longer here—they demanded that I should tell you to telephone them immediately you returned."

Apparently the call had come from the Headquarters of the Frauenwerke, where I had already gone to be put in touch with anything of interest, journalistically speaking. It was they who had sent me to Hibaudi and had furnished me with a list of stores selling modern German handicrafts. Frau Schmolke, with her usual frankness, admitted that one reason why the message had gone out of her head was dislike of the organization as such.

"Twenty million women—imagine it. All banded together, for what? Young chits with their hair but lately coiled about their ears telling us what to eat and how to cook it! Let them stay in their own homes and mind their own businesses!"

I went to the telephone and rang them up. I did not want to give Frau Schmolke away, so omitted to mention that I had been back in Berlin for some time already. The cool, crisp voice which replied might have belonged to any one of the women whom I had spoken to there before going to Riga. It seemed to know all about me, and to require nothing more than my name and address to identify my needs and interests.

The voice said that it would like me to meet a very intelligent English gentleman who happened to be living in Berlin, conducting classes in his own language. The entire Frauenwerke

could guarantee the gentleman's respectability and willingness
to be helpful to strangers from his own country who might wish
to ask questions which would be impartially answered in
English.

I could not think of any questions that I wished answered at
the moment, and said so. The voice sharpened. Surely, as a
travelling journalist, I would want to be informed about quite a
number of things ! My German was not very good, I had said
so myself. But apart from the convenience of being able to discuss matters freely in my own language, a Britisher resident in
Berlin would be far more likely to tell the truth about matters
in Germany today, because he would view them objectively,
nicht ?

I hung up the receiver, puzzled.

Half an hour later there was another telephone call for me.
A Mr Smith. The Frauenwerke lady had said the Englishman's
name was Smith. He sounded nervous, as well he might. He
phrased his words well enough, although speaking with an un-
educated Cockney accent which I hoped he did not hand on to
his pupils. But even the phrasing might not be his own. It
sounded more like the mechanical repetition of a message which
he had only just received himself.

He hawped I would excuse the liberty. He understood that
the Secretary at the headquarters of the Frauenwerke had telephoned to recommend him. Was there anything I would like
to be shown, or any information I would like to be given before
I went back to England?

Of course. Mr Smith must be a professional guide. No doubt
he combined that with his teaching of English. But I had no
money to indulge in guides, and preferred to do without them,
anyway.

When I had said this as tactfully as possible, there followed
a long pause at the other end of the telephone. There was an
urgent quality about that pause, and I realized what it meant
when Mr Smith spoke again. For some inexplicable reason he
was frightened.

"But you have no objection to our meeting, perhaps just

once, for coffee? It was not my fault that you had gone to Riga when I telephoned the first time! I did what I could. . . ."

His agitation intrigued me. We arranged to meet that afternoon in a small café half-way along the Kurfürstendamm.

It was early in the afternoon and the café was half-empty. I could easily spot Mr Smith. He was a little man somewhere in his thirties with a white and anxious face, and a shiny dark blue suit worn with a bow-tie. The effect, however, was not jaunty, but drab. No matter how long he might have lived abroad, he still belonged to the London lunch-hour, the suburban train service, Lyons Corner House, and the tube escalators at the rush hour.

Conversation was sticky at first. My coming from Scotland was an obvious disappointment to him, since it removed the possibility of our finding common ground. He had never been to Scotland, and said so with no great regret. We sipped our coffee, eyeing each other thoughtfully. . . .

Then Mr Smith gathered courage and plunged. I wrote for the papers, didn't I? Then it was time somebody told the truth about what was happening in Germany today. Germany was setting its house in order, and setting an example to the world as well. Thanks to institutions like the Frauenwerke, the One-Dish-Sunday organization, and so on, the poor and needy were being clothed, social abuses were being stopped, mothers were being encouraged to feed their children properly so that a strong, healthy race would result.

As for art and things of the spirit; well, the Führer was an artist himself and he knew what was what. Certain forms of art (which, Mr Smith was sorry to say, still flourished in London and Paris) were absolutely forbidden in Germany today. And a jolly good thing too. Who wanted to look at woman with eyes on different levels and not a stitch on?

And take music. Was I fond of music? He was glad to hear it, because he always held that anyone who didn't like music had a Want. The Führer had excellent ideas about music too. He had forbidden American jazz, which was mere negro hysteria, and he gave his support to many a deserving young composer who would have had to wait long enough for recognition without it.

I might have swallowed this last statement whole, if it had not been for the remembrance of the feeble music written by one of Hitler's protégés in place of Mendelssohn's. Then, too, Gertrude's bitter remark, that her lack of employment was due to her not holding a Party ticket, stuck in my mind and throat.

So I asked whether the young composers favoured by Herr Hitler were only deserving if they belonged to the Party? And what, incidentally, about the ban on Mendelssohn? Was his music, at least, not deserving?

Curiously enough, Mr Smith brightened up. It was as if he had been studying the answers to these very questions, and I had disappointed him, up to now, by not asking them. Naturally artists and musicians wishing to receive help from the State must give it too. That was logical, wasn't it? You don't give a fellow a grant or help to put his opera on, and leave him quite free to undermine your influence and try to get you out of power! Stands to reason, doesn't it?

And, put that way, it *did* seem to stand to reason.

As for Mendelssohn and all them Jews, Mr Smith went on, getting more intense and rather excited, well, some of them might be all right, but how were you to know? Jews were always dangerous, right through history they were. Did I know that at one time whole boatloads of them had been sent out of England? In the reign of one of the Edwards, Mr Smith thought it was. And there was a tower in York, where about six hundred Jews had been pushed off and massacred. So who were we to talk?

Besides, nowadays, more's the pity, the British aristocracy was riddled with Jewish blood. You just had to look at the photos of some of the women in the smart society papers. All the big families would have been ruined long ago if it hadn't been for Jewish money and Jewish marriages. Can you wonder that England makes the most noise about the Jews being asked to leave Germany?

His anxious face peered at mine across the table. I couldn't think why he seemed so urgent about the matters he touched upon. But now, for the first time since coming to Berlin, I felt a little frightened myself. Though of what?

"Have you been back in England lately?" I asked, just to change the conversation. But that was a mistake. At the personal question, he shrank still more and a look of suspicion leapt into his eyes.

"Me? What makes you think I'd go back there? I've got my living to get, here in Berlin, see?"

I said I was afraid it was time to go. He made no move to call the waiter, but the man, seeing me gather my things together, brought the bill and laid it between us. Mr Smith did not pick it up, so I did. He looked a little shamefaced at that and mumbled his thanks. At the door of the café we parted, and I saw his slim, shabby figure melt into the crowds as if he were anxious to hide it even from himself.

Mr Smith had puzzled me and left me with a disagreeable impression. At supper that night I recounted some of the things he had said. They were greeted with mirth, especially the bit about the Führer's taste in music.

The chorus-master told me, in his slightly prim, old-maidish way, the latest story going the rounds of Berlin. The Führer (accompanied by Goering, whose passion for gaudy uniforms was a standing joke) had gone together to see *Lohengrin*. The Führer, tired out by his weight of responsibility, fell asleep. He was rudely awakened by the burst of music heralding Lohengrin's arrival, bright in shining armour and borne in on the back of his swan. Startled, he muttered to his friend, "You've gone too far this time, Hermann!"

We all laughed.

"But what about the Jews?" I asked.

The laughter died uncomfortably. "He went too far there too," said Gertrud at last. "We have many good Jewish merchant families in Hamburg who are loyal citizens of Germany —people just like ourselves."

"Of course!" Frau Schmolke nodded her massively coiffed head. "Here, too. I have had many good friends among the old

Jewish families of Berlin. Nobody had a word to say against *them*! It was the low, unscrupulous type of Jew which poured in over the Polish frontier after the war that should be packed off. Already they have dug their finger-nails into everything and pulled down standards of honesty everywhere. . . ."

"Then would it not have been a good idea to banish these Jews—the ones who came into the country after 1918—and let the others remain?"

Everyone nodded and said, "Of course." But Gertrud smiled and added, "The reason that was not done lies in a flaw in our national character. We are too thorough by far!"

At intervals during the short while that remained, I puzzled over Mr Smith and his telephone call. But it was nearly time for me to go back to Scotland and spend the winter writing up my experiences and perhaps attacking the idea of a novel. There were travel arrangements to make, packing to arrange, good-byes to be said.

"But, Liebe Elisabeth, we shall see you back, surely! Everyone comes back to the Pension Schmolke!"

I promised them that I would return next year. Next year perhaps I would start out on my adventures sooner; visit Central Europe, and even go farther east, towards the musical comedy countries of the Balkans. Every European state was making strong bids for the tourist traffic which brought dollars or sterling, and one, in these days, was as good as the other. Journalists had a happy time, even free-lance beginners like myself. If there was the smallest possibility of their articles being used at home, then free passes on the railways, opera and theatre tickets, and vouchers for most things were theirs. But even then, I had a dim feeling that the sun would not shine for ever; that hay had better be gathered before the wind rose.

The hot stuffiness of the streets had gone. There was a nip in the air now, and Frau Schmolke was talking of getting out the billowing winter quilts. She had forgotten to take down the notice about dogs not being allowed; and a day or two before my departure I saw a new intimation, a small hand-bill, pinned up beside it, along with a fresh crop of intimations about winter concerts.

This one gave the programme of the forthcoming recital by the eminent pianist, Paul Kiss. It was to take place on the date of my departure. I was actually walking downstairs to the waiting taxi when the Prodigal Son returned. He passed me, lugging two suitcases and stumbling eagerly upward and homeward towards the Pension Schmolke.

10

I WAS in a second-class carriage of a train made up of old-fashioned coaches which had belonged to the rolling-stock under the old Austrian Empire. I had spent spring and most of summer in Hungary and Transylvania, which had once formed parts of that Empire. The double-headed Eagle of the Habs-burgs had become a familiar symbol of vanished splendour. During Austrian domination, it had seemed a bird of prey to many citizens of the Empire. Now, when the old-fashioned Hungarian or Transylvanian looked backwards over his shoul-der to the days before 1914, he was apt to speak as though the Eagle's wings had been tipped with gold.

So when I told my Hungarian friends of the journey I must make between Belgrade and Bosnia, which was once an Austrian province, they were ready with advice. Some of them went to Bosnia still, for the mineral springs there gave excellent cures. They went because travel and living were cheap in the Yugoslavia carved out of the old Empire. But they went with bitter hearts, and scorn of the haphazard way things were run in the new Succession States. Especially the way the railways were run.

However, it had appeared that, by catching one certain train from Belgrade and proceeding all night to Serajevo, one might still taste a civilized mode of travel. For Yugoslavia had not yet got around to scrapping all the old railway coaches which had happened to be within her borders when the war broke out. The double-headed Eagle and the "K. und K." had been obliterated from their sides, but their elegance and comfort were the same, though perhaps some of the springs might be a little weak....

So I was swaying and rattling through the night in a car-riage the like of which had scarcely been seen since the Old

Emperor died. (They were pretty old-fashioned even then.) Deep cushioned seats, like double arm-chairs, faced each other in pairs down one side of each coach, the other side being kept clear as a passage-way. The train being only half-full, I was able to annex a pair of seats, a small square of territory, to myself, as everyone else was doing.

A little distance out of Belgrade, when dusk had deepened into night, the elderly conductor made his way down the coach, saluting each passenger with the slightly formal courtesy which had been the hall-mark of an official under the old "K. und K." He then bent down and, pulling out an extension from beneath the double arm-chair facing the engine, joined it to the seat of the one opposite, thus making a comfortable bed. Then he straightened up again, and reached for the pair of heavy grey curtains hanging from a brass curtain pole above each pair of seats. By day they were tied back, but now he released them and drew them together with a jangling of metal rings. And there you were, in a tiny, comfortable sleeping-apartment where undressing could be done in perfect privacy.

So I reached Serajevo. The name still echoes like a pistol shot to those whose childhood was interrupted by the war of 1914. Serajevo. We learned that the J was sounded like a Y (who told us? There were no radio announcers then), and everything which had clouded our young happiness seemed to have started there. Fathers and brothers in khaki; Zeppelins, food shortages, no more parties with ice-cream and conjurers, and, for years after the war stopped, not enough partners at dances to go round.

Because the Archduke Franz-Ferdinand, nephew of the Emperor of Austria, had been shot in this town which was only a name. There were photographs in the papers at the time, and again, during the years after the war, when politicians and war correspondents began to write their memoirs, with illustrations. Photographs of a heavy-jowled, pop-eyed man with a dark moustache; and sometimes photographs of his wife as well (for she had been killed too), who was named "morganatic" in a puzzling fashion, and was only a plain Duchess without the Arch.

No one knew now whether, in ordering his nephew to make a State visit to the capital of the newly annexed province of Bosnia, the Old Emperor had deliberately sent him to his death. Franz-Ferdinand had always made trouble for his uncle. He had even threatened to upset the absolutism of Habsburg rule by openly promising some form of Federal Government to his wife's country, Bohemia, as soon as he should come to the throne. Was it not said that the Emperor's first words, on hearing of the tragedy, were, "God has restored the balance I have tried to maintain"?

A dull and stuffy pair who had done their duty and been shot for it. Yet they were somehow real to me, because, in the course of my wanderings, I had visited their small hunting castle in Bohemia which the new Czechoslovak government had opened as a holiday home for guests of the State. Their furniture, ordered wholesale from Maples, still stood in the rooms, brass bedsteads, ruched lamps and all; as characterless and Edwardian as themselves. But it was their home. And the faded photographs of their friends and their shooting-parties still stood around in elaborate silver frames, shadowy mementoes of an era which had belonged to my childhood.

The other day I dropped in to a cinema where they were showing bits of old news reels. And there, starting out on their last drive, were the Archduke and his wife. The old-fashioned automobile moved across the screen; the fat, pompous figure lifted its hand to its plumed hat in salute, and the tight-lipped, fringed figure beside it bowed her head stiffly from side to side, making the ostrich feathers nod around her wide-brimmed hat. There was a flicker and a break in the reel. And once more I felt the swing of the old Austrian carriage beneath me; heard the jangle of the curtain rings above my head. . . .

But Serajevo, when I got there, was just a big, ramshackle modern town. Its architecture still bore the Austrian impress, and I was disappointed at the lack of Oriental flavour in the capital of a province which, with its large Turkish population, was said to have clung to the fez and the yashmak after Turkey proper had given them up. Only the bazaar showed me what I wanted to see, and there the lane of the coppersmiths proved most fascinating. I wanted a copper tray, but could find none large enough. But an elderly Turk who sat cross-legged hammering them out, showed by the circumference of his arms, that he understood the size I wanted. So I paid him, and in the evening a small boy arrived at my hotel, bowling the tray before him like a hoop.

The noise of the traffic, the horns of the motor-buses, and the blare of the hotel band kept me awake for long. At last I dropped off, to be awakened again, this time by the stillness of dawn. A pinkish light flushed the plaster on the opposite wall from my bed. A little, recurrent noise broke the stillness; a noise obliterated during the day, though it must have lulled me all night. And then a voice, from high up and far away, calling something in a quarter-note scale like a melodious, unearthly quaver.

It was the voice of the Hodja on the minaret of the great mosque next to the hotel. The other noise was the dripping of the fountain in the courtyard before the mosque. And I knew that Bosnia's legacy from the East was still there for me to discover, overlaid though it was in the daytime by the modern bustle of a Succession State.

It was the old Turkish life that I wanted to see. Modern Turkey had discarded it, but it still lingered here in Bosnia, once a Turkish province, then an Austrian, and now part of modern Yugoslavia. At home in Scotland during the winter, I had heard of a fellow Scotswoman, married and living in Bosnia, who would be prepared to put me up for a few weeks in summer. And I was on my way to her now.

The little branch-line from Serajevo ran through a wide valley with a line of mountains in the distance. Now, when the height of summer had begun to curve towards autumn, the land looked bare and dry, so that one's throat parched in looking at it. The mountains swung a little nearer, but they were jagged and cruel. How could there be any town here, much less a town anteceding Serajevo as the old Turkish capital; a town important enough to be the seat of Pashas for two hundred years?

And then, suddenly, the train ran right into it. There it lay, right under the hills, where hidden springs or gathered rains turned it into an oasis of greenery. The Turks called it Travnik, or Grassytown. Even now, at this dry, fag-end of the season, a freshness lay over it; a scent of flowers floated over the walls of the hidden gardens, and the innumerable minarets pointed their white fingers above the town like lilies.

And there, on the platform waiting to greet me, were my host and hostess. Arthur Meissner belonged to the short-lived Austrian era of Travnik. When the Empire annexed both Bosnia and Herzegovina, his grandfather had come here as one of the newly appointed State officials. The journey from Vienna had been made by waggon, since the railroad was not then built; and the grandson of this Empire builder could still show the pistols, hanging crossed on his wall, which had protected his grandparents during their long trek south.

Now, after the war and the crumbling of the Empire, he had stayed on here. Where else could he go? Besides, he had a good business in the district as a road contractor and engineer. The Slavs and Mohammedans might wish to be free, but they had not yet learned to do without Austrian skill and integrity.

So Arthur Meissner was popular, and he stayed on.

They greeted me kindly, those two fair, Western creatures, with their grey eyes and their hearty kindness. They bundled me into their old-fashioned open victoria, and drove me first through the fairly modern part of the town where the buildings resembled block-houses and the view was dominated by the huge bulk of the Jesuit Seminary built in the Austrian days.

But soon the horse turned of its own will into a narrow side-path. Now all life was hidden behind high walls and pierced lattices, for we had entered the old Turkish quarter. Here many handsome houses, once belonging to wealthy Turkish land-owners in the district, stood decaying quietly behind those walls. But some had been taken over and rehabilitated by families who knew the value of space and beautiful craftsmanship.

The horse stopped at a gateway with a half-obliterated inscription in Arabic carved on the wall beside it. The giant doors sealing the entrance had great bronze handles such as I was to see on many doors in Travnik, and all more or less of the same pattern. The doors opened stiffly, making a harsh sound against the sharp cobbles of the courtyard within. I looked up at the plaster walls of the old house, and saw how its whole upper story bulged forward to accommodate an oriel window filled with tiny panes of leaded glass. And the glass twinkled and flashed in the setting sun so that one could not bear to look at it.

Down from the house sloped the garden towards the river. At its farthest end stood the shut-up crumbling little mosque which had belonged to the Turkish family who had once lived here. Around it sprang a tangle of grass, blue-green and rich because of the moisture under the soil. And across the grass where it had fallen lay the minaret belonging to the mosque, its whiteness now mottled and stained with mould.

The door of the house stood open. I walked in, and up a great staircase which curved gracefully, bordered by a balustrade of elaborately carved, pierced woodwork. I was led into a white-washed room with many embroidered cushions piled on the bed, and a black bearskin rug on the floor.

"I hope you will be comfortable here," Mrs Meissner said with her friendly smile. "Don't drop anything you value because the floor slopes from east to west, and things are apt to roll out of sight."

THE outer wall of the courtyard ran just underneath my window. I could therefore look down on the street below and on the motley figures that passed to and fro. First thing in the morning I was awakened by the tramp of boots, hard and steady as a drill on the cobbles outside. The soldiers from the barracks were passing by.

Then, as the sky brightened and the air got warmer, the peasants from the country shuffled beneath my window, their bare feet making slip-slop noises. They generally stopped to slake their thirst at the wall fountain beside the gate, and if they carried livestock they dropped the hens or piglings being brought to market with a fleshy thud on the cobbles, and the voice of the outraged creatures screamed through the gurgle of the fountain itself.

A little later, when enough custom would be gathered in the town square to make his arrival worth-while, the Sladolid man would pass under my window, with a jangling of metal and ringing of bells. I called him that from his cry, which he began to practise before he had got out of earshot at the other end of the lane. Sladolid! Slado-Lid! He would clear his throat and sing, *sotto voce,* experimentally. . . . He bore a curious brass vessel strapped to his shoulders. It had many jangling decorations, and little spouts out of which came, I believe, some sort of sugared drink. The whole contraption, with its metal excrescences, its jewelled inlets of blue and red glass, was so obviously germ-laden that even when I encountered the Sladolid man later in the day, I never had the courage to stop him and discover the taste of the brew he carried.

By this time Travnik had wakened up properly. The air would grow steadily warmer, and one was thankful to be in a house built by an Eastern architect who understood the value of thick walls and vaulted ceilings. However hard the sun blazed outside, inside there was coolness and quiet. Mr Meissner had long since gone out to supervise some building operation elsewhere in the neighbourhood. At lunch-time he would return, and we would eat in the room with the oriel window and the great window-seat which curved round it like a half-moon. Eat dishes prepared from old Austrian recipes brought from Vienna long ago, or Scotch ones brought from Scotland yesterday. A great deal of mutton, pastry made of paper-thin layers, and always the thimbleful of thick, sweet Turkish coffee to finish the meal.

And then the siesta, when even the lane on the other side of the wall grew quiet at last, and the whole world slept. The sun began to incline until it shone on the rusty Crescent on the dome of the little mosque at the end of the garden. The water, half-glimpsed as it ran past the mosque and threaded each garden on its way through the town, now caught the light and glittered. And some colour stole back faintly to the irises growing between the flags of the path leading down to the river.

I woke up and yawned. Everyone in Travnik was probably doing the same thing; getting ready for the chief social hour of the day, still called, all over what was once the old Austrian Empire, the Corso. This charming habit was the one remaining link between the broken pieces of the Empire; the one delightful legacy which even the most nationalistic of the Succession States refused to give up. It was a simple form of pleasure, costing no more than the price of a cup of coffee or a glass of wine, and it lay, therefore, within the reach of the humblest family in any of the smaller towns stretching from Middle Europe east and south towards the Adriatic.

The true Corso spirit must have been specially fostered by the Habsburgs as a variant of the Bread and Circuses tradition. I had seen it at work, only a week or two before, in the Transylvanian garrison town of Sibiu. The town contained three national elements : Hungarian, Rumanian, and Saxon. By day they had their quarrels and kept to opposite camps. Indeed, without the soothing nightly bromide of the Corso, they might have come to bloodshed. But Sibiu contained only one principal street, wide and flower-decked, following the line of the old ramparts. One could not stroll up and down it on pleasure bent, without at least learning to tolerate the right of others to do the same.

The café proprietors, however nationalistic they might be, had to consider their pockets and order their orchestras to play Hungarian Czardas, Rumanian Hola music, and the old German folk-tunes in strict rotation. The musicians themselves did not object, for they were gypsies, anyway, and to them the music of one race was as good as that of another so long as it *was* music. So night darkened over a thousand Main Streets south and east of Vienna. Over a thousand interwoven sounds; the sounds of the Rumanian officers' spurs against the Sibiu sidewalk, over the Italian opera airs being discoursed on piazzas bordering the Adriatic, and the high, wavering call of the Hodja of Travnik as, breathless from his long climb up the minaret stairs, he stood beneath an evening sky, calling upon the faithful to pause and remember God.

The call came towards us faintly, weirdly, as we stepped, the three of us, through the heavy gateway and entered the lane which ran by the wall of the house. We passed beneath the bulging lattices which masked the harem quarters belonging to the other old houses along the lane. Many of them were shut up and abandoned. A few families still lingered on, pure-bred Turks mostly, descendants of some vizier's retinue and not the Slav Moslems, whom one could distinguish at once (the men at any rate) by their blue eyes and square features under the fez they still clung to. The women were indistinguishable from each other, since both Slav and Oriental wore balloon-like trousered shrouds of gaudy cotton, with the ritual square of black net falling over the face.

We came out of the lane and entered the main street of the town. By day it was dull enough. Only the glass windows of the Club and the peeling plaster minaret of the great mosque diversified the line of two-storied modern stucco houses, for this part of Travnik had been rebuilt after the modern Balkan style which aped America. But now the half-light blurred their boxy outlines, veiling the drabness of the street.

The Hodja was finishing his call as we passed by the mosque, now opened and lit up. It is better to pray than to sleep. . . . The words fell down warningly upon us from that great height above like drops of icy water. But it seemed as if few Moslems were prepared to listen. Only a few old men carefully removed their boots in the courtyard before disappearing into its lighted depths. The young men, Slav or Oriental, stood about in knots or called out greetings in the Corso spirit, indifferent to the warning cry. For them a cup of coffee and a gossip were evidently preferable to prayer.

"They have lost the habit," said my host. "They don't need Kemal Ataturk to teach them to turn their backs on religion. It is the spirit of the age."

"Then Moslem customs have relaxed even here?" I asked. "In spite of governmental tolerance of the mosque and the yashmak?"

Mr Meissner's fat, jolly face smiled through the dusk. "The yashmak's going too. Ladies must all be in the fashion nowadays." His smile died away. He looked pensive. "The old ways were better," he added. "Yes, though I am a Catholic, I must say so. Indeed, the old ways are nearly always better, are they not?"

"Arthur means," his Scots wife put in, "that now the Moslem taboos have been put aside, the morals of the town have not improved. In the old days, when every woman wore a yashmak and to go unveiled was a shame, there were no prostitutes in the streets. Now one sees them here, and still more in Serajevo. When no orthodox Moslem tasted wine, it was a nine-days wonder to come across one drunk. Now it is not so uncommon."

We had begun to pace the middle of the road like the others. The dry dust flew up chokingly into our nostrils, stirred by the feet of the whole populace, passing and repassing. Windows had been flung up along the whole length of the street, and there, above our heads, an audience sat gossiping and munching sweets, leaning its elbows on the cushions placed along the sills and calling down badinage to its friends below.

Most of that audience was composed of women and children, Turkish or Sephardim Jews debarred by their orthodoxy from mixing with the crowd in the street. The Jewish women leaned over curiously, their peaked and braided hats like shaped grocers' bags nodding above heads shaven on marriage according to their particular custom. Their voices sounded harshly above the murmur of the crowd as they shouted their news from one window to the next.

One came across little pockets of Sephardim Jews here and there in the Balkans. They were descendants of the Spanish Jews scattered by the Inquisition in the sixteenth century, and they still spoke Spanish amongst themselves. They did not seem to incite the same loathing and dread as the Galician Jew did farther north. But they were the aristocracy of the Hebrew world; the stock from which our own Montefiores and Disraelis had sprung.

Through the fine new windows of the Club, now brilliantly lighted, we could see the card-players bent over their little tables. An Orthodox priest was among them. The street lamps brought out the red gleam of the carbuncle in the cross hanging over his greasy soutane. His hands, grimed with field work, held the still grimier cards. There was a tax of about thirty shillings on all playing-cards in Yugoslavia, which pushed their price up to over two pounds. Only rich families owned a pack of their own. The others hired them from some café by the hour, as the players were doing now.

The Turks preferred to play chess. They played it impassively, interminably. We could see groups of them doing so, sitting beneath the tree which sheltered their own outdoor Kafana. It was built about the tomb of a long-dead vizier which provided a grassy but inconvenient oasis just at an angle in the busiest part of the street. The enclosed space, however, could not be built over because of strong Moslem views on the subject of sacrilege.

We went across to it, and sat down at a little table set in the long grass. A thimbleful of Turkish coffee was placed before each of us and, accompanying it, a lump of Turkish Delight, heavy with nuts and speared through with a useful tooth-pick to keep one's fingers from getting sticky as one ate. Some water from an iron spout trickled into a trough by the side of the vizier's grave. Here the faithful might wash their feet before pausing to say their prayers under the domed roof of the grave. But no worshippers came while we sat there, and the fountain was only used by the little boy waiter who ran out at intervals with an apronful of dirty coffee-cups, which he rinsed in the trough.

From the dark grove where we sat, we could see across the road to the Christian café, outside of which men sat at little tables playing Török. Among the couples were the young doctor and his assistant from the grand new hospital recently erected in the town.

"They have plenty to do at that hospital." Mr Meissner remarked. "People are constantly being taken there after trying to commit suicide by drinking spirits of salt."

His wife nodded.

"It is a very favourite form of taking one's life here."

"Of course," he went on, "in the old days, if a doctor had happened to be in the café playing Török when he was sent for to save a would-be suicide, he would never dream of interrupting his game. They don't sometimes, even now."

"In any case," put in his wife gently, "death here is not considered such a very serious thing."

The Corso was drawing to its close. The street was emptying, its endless surge of feet travelling up and down, now ceasing gradually. Here and there a window slammed shut. One by one the cushions were withdrawn from the sills, and the nodding heads of the Jewesses had vanished. One might have heard the Hodja's cry more clearly now, but he was silent and the moon had swung clear of the vast dome of the mosque, mirroring itself in the basin at the foot of the fountain in its courtyard; the fountain whose gentle drip-drip sounded like a tap insufficiently turned off.

We passed it on our way home. The white wall of the lane caught the moonlight which shone on a thin stream of water falling from the little wall fountain, turning it into a stem of glass. A sliver of moonlight showed between the two black gates. "I forgot to close them properly," Mr Meissner exclaimed, annoyed with himself.

Inside the courtyard, the moon had caught the front of the house as well. The leaded panes of the oriel window shone like diamonds this time instead of gold. The hall door stood open. The great staircase swept up in curves of blackness towards a black and shadowy roof. At its foot stood a garden chair, always kept there in readiness for anyone who wanted to carry it out and sit by the river. And from this chair there arose, at our approach, the figure of an elderly Turk.

I think we all got a fright. Mr Meissner said something in tones which clearly meant, "What is the meaning of this?"

The old Turk bowed with dignity and said something back. Then, without undue haste, he made his departure. The Meissners laughed. I asked what he had said.

He had said he was tired and, seeing the gate to the courtyard open, had come inside, meaning to rest in peace and quiet. But when he saw the chair, the thought had struck him that it would be interesting to sit on it and experience what it felt like to be a Christian gentleman.

12

It was true, what Mrs Meissner had said. Human life, here in
Travnik, was not valued on quite the same scale as with us. It
was not, for example, valued as high as a wooden fence.

One had only to glance at the countryside to realize how precious timber must be. There was a certain fascination about
the tawny landscape, but no shade. Even an oasis like Travnik,
watered by its river and musical with many springs and fountains, lacked the heavy shade of trees big enough to be worth
cutting down. Here, behind great garden walls, grew delicate
fruit trees and trembling acacias which cast a grateful flicker
of green. But they were far too precious to be used for timber.

So when Jusef Hassanovic's trial for the murder of Mustafa
Bilic burst on Travnik, everyone was sympathetic to the murderer who had, quite rightly, shot Bilic dead for destroying his
wooden fence. Day after day Hassanovic was driven from the
old Austrian prison to the courthouse, where he stood up and
put his point of view, with dignity, before a kindly judge, who
knew well the exorbitant cost of enough wood to fence round
one's fields.

Visitors to the Meissners' house discussed the trial day by
day. The case seemed to be getting another trial; one which
took into consideration more facts than were allowed to be
openly mentioned at the trial itself. And the judgment of the
whole neighbourhood, which was unanimous, was based on its
knowledge of the characters of the two men. Only Mr Meissner,
in whose bones stirred the inherited impartiality of Austrian
rule, and his wife and myself, accustomed to the shibboleths of
Western law, were a little uncomfortable. A life for a life. And
yet . . .

Jusef Hassanovic was a poor man. In order to fence his little
pocket of land around and prevent his livestock from straying,

he had to buy new timber, and the price of it took every penny he had. Unfortunately a rich neighbour, Mustafa Bilic, had got into the habit of driving his ox-waggon diagonally right across Hassanovic's plot of land, in order to cut off a corner and shorten the way to his own fields.

Next time Bilic came that way after the fence was built, he drove his oxen right through it rather than turn and go back by the road. The beast's horns had uprooted the staples Hassanovic had taken so long to make out of his precious timber, and the heavy waggon had left a pile of matchwood behind it. Hassanovic had rushed out of his house, shouting. And Bilic had only laughed. . . .

Hassanovic didn't think of seeking redress by law. He was frightened of lawyers' fees, and of what Bilic might do to him afterwards by way of reprisal. He spent two days away from his work, scouring the bare Bosnian hillsides for a few worm-eaten scraps of wood. With what he could find, he had spent another day making some sort of lattice work to fill in the torn gap in the fence, to protect his vegetables and his hens. And then, shortly afterwards, he had come home at dusk after a hard day's work in the fields, to find a rent wide enough to let in a herd of buffalo, in a new place this time, so that more of his good, sound wood lay in white splinters on the grass.

This time he said nothing at all. He merely stood where he was and waited until his wife had run back to the house for the old-fashioned long-barrelled gun which hung on the wall above the stove. With the gun in his hand to show he meant business, he walked across to the Bilics' low-eaved, wooden-tiled house. They laughed, even while he showed them the gun and told them that next time he would shoot to kill. They had been to Belgrade, both father and son, and had grown quite sophisticated. They had forgotten that some people still clung to old-fashioned methods of justice.

The next time they drove out in the ox-waggon he was at home, waiting for them to come that way. He heard them crash through the fence, walked to the door of his house and from there shot them both dead as they sat puppet-like on top of a load of hay. They had actually fallen from it on top of the fence, where they hung, spreadeagled, until the police arrived. Hassanovic was quite ready to go away with the police and state his case to folk who, like himself, knew relative values of men and timber in a land where timber is scarce.

The minimum sentence for murder allowed by law was two years' imprisonment, which was what Hassanovic got. Even that seemed to have sent a shock of indignation through the town. The widow of the man who was shot did not dare to wail too loudly, I was told. Everyone knew who had given first provocation and to whom sympathy was due. But the wife of the prisoner had to hire herself out for the whole summer in order to pay for enough wood to mend the fence once again.

When all the excitement died down, Travnik fell back into its pleasant torpor, diversified by a little mild social life which mostly circulated round the Serbian officers and their wives who had come here with the Serb regiment posted to the barracks.

The better-class Turks were little in evidence in the communal life of the place. It was a bitter pill for them when their estates had been cut up and their power broken. Those who had not withdrawn to Turkey itself lived secluded lives and kept their wives and daughters strictly shut in. If they could possibly afford it, they sent their sons to school in France or Switzerland, and had them finished off at the old Arabic College in Stamboul. To spend money in educating one's daughters was still thought a fantastic and sinful waste.

So the only Turkish women I came in contact with—the only ones encountered freely when shopping or at the Corso— were the daughters of Akim Beg. They were different because he was different. He was a modern man of the world who admired Ataturk and had decided that, in Travnik at least, the position of Moslem women must be improved.

"But he makes a big mistake," Mr Meissner said. "Such things as female education and going unveiled may be all very well for Angora, but they will not do for Travnik. We are conservative here."

"Even Akim Beg would like to see his daughters married," said Mrs Meissner, smiling slightly. "But the young Turks of good family who live about here are suspicious of learned women. They may tolerate lipstick in Paris, but not here."

"His wife does not approve either," her husband said. "She would like to have brought up Baba and Fatima as she was brought up herself, and I think she is a little afraid of the smart clothes she has to wear to please Akim Beg. But one part, at least, of the old law remains—she has to obey him!"

I became anxious to meet this emancipated Turkish family that seemed so out of place among the ruins of a Moslem past which had been swept away elsewhere. And I was glad when they invited us to drive out, one late afternoon when the sun's heat had cooled a little, to a Turkish garden on the outskirts of the town.

Perhaps the name sounds more alluring than the fact. It simply means that some Turk, more enterprising than most, had rented a field or dusty patch of grass, if possible shaded by a bush or two, and within sound of the river. Here he had placed a few backless wooden benches with trestle tables before them, had wired the field round, and then stationed a member of his family at the opening to exact a trifling fee for entry. If some itinerant musician liked to take up his place there too, all the better. The music would serve as an orchestra to accompany the hot, syrupy coffee ordered by each comer. It was all there was to order. But those who drove or walked out of the town for a little air were welcome to bring their own refreshments, and they usually did.

We had spent an hour first at Akim Beg's modern villa, built according to modern American ideas and complete with up-to-date plumbing on the side of a hill, a little beyond the town. Then I was invited to drive with Madame and her two daughters, while Akim himself got into the Meissners' carriage.

The road was exceedingly stony, and we were thrown from side to side, while the inch or two of black net, attached to Madame Akim's smart little hat instead of a yashmak, quivered and rippled incessantly over the bridge of her nose. Her two daughters were not veiled at all. They were hatless, Fatima with a round blue comb holding her hair back, Baba with a coquettish half-circle of rosebuds stitched on a ribbon. They wore dirndl dresses with short puffed sleeves, and open sandals showing their lacquered and polished toe-nails.

They were well educated; spoke French and English besides Arabic and Serb, and they had been to a boarding-school in Lausanne. They chattered incessantly as we drove along, but their mother understood only when French was used. The rest of the time she sat silent, the rings on her plump little hands sparkling through her black net gloves.

The so-called garden was, as I expected, no Arabian Nights' Dream, but merely a dusty field such as the others I had already visited. It was somewhat nearer the river than they had been, so gained the advantage of a row of willows growing along its bank. The willows were stunted and knobbed, and made excellent coat-stands. Already they were festooned with garments which hung grotesquely above the water, dripping sleeves like catkins. Immediately the two men had got down from the other carriage, they too made for the willows to hang up their coats and hats as in some suburban hall-way. Then, in their shirt-sleeves like everyone else because of the heat, they commandeered a table and two benches, and escorted us gravely towards them.

The clientele was as mixed as the population of Travnik itself. There was a party of Sephardim Jews, the women wearing those hideous embroidered bags like tea-cosies upon their heads. There was the school-inspector from Belgrade with his fluffy, over-dressed little wife. A party of Serb officers from the barracks made their corner of the field noisy with talk and laughter. Mostly people sat almost silent. Down at the gate, two Turkish fiddlers played sad, interminable little airs which seemed always the same air, wavering up and down.

Mrs Meissner directed my attention to a Turkish family opposite, telling me in an undertone that they were cousins of Akim Beg's. Baba and Fatima had spoken already of them in the carriage, wondering if they would be here. They were incredibly old-fashioned and behind the times, I was told. Poor Aledja, who was sixteen already, was never allowed anywhere without her parents, and never unveiled! Nor had she been sent abroad. She had been kept at home with no education at all. . . .

I could not possibly tell which was Aledja. There seemed to be several women in that family, but they were not only closely veiled, they were so wrapped up in spite of the warm evening that one could scarcely guess at their ages. Moreover, they perched like hens right up on their bench, with their heels tucked in under them. Every veiled Turkish woman was doing the same. It made them more shapeless than ever.

"And she's quite pretty too!" Fatima said.

Presently Aledja's father came over to speak to his cousin. There was a good deal of visiting in this way, and I noticed it was considered courteous, on the part of those who sat at tables with foodstuffs before them, to break off half a pastry, or the leg and wing of chicken, and offer it as a parting gift when the visitor was about to withdraw.

Aledja's father came right over to Akim Beg and stood beside him, talking without a glance at any of us except Mr Meissner, whom he politely included in the conversation now and then. We were women and therefore, by his old-fashioned code, must be ignored. But Fatima and Baba did not seem to mind. They were eagerly eyeing a handsome young Turk who had just driven up to the entrance in an expensive-looking car, and, after tossing a coin towards the two fiddlers, had entered the garden.

He paid no attention to them whatever. But when Aledja's father had finished his conversation, had bowed his thanks for the sticky lump of sweetmeat handed to him as though he were a schoolboy, and had withdrawn, the young Turk got up hastily to intercept him on his way back to his own table. So far as I could see, the newcomer did not even glance at the row of female shapes roosting on the bench towards which the other man was making his way. But the eyes of Fatima and Baba grew suddenly watchful. And their mother drew in her breath with a sharp hiss.

"She can't even count properly!" Baba exclaimed.

Akim Beg, in the midst of the dissertation upon modern Turkey to which he was treating me, stopped in bewilderment. "Who cannot count properly?" he asked.

"Aledja. Thanks to her old-fashioned upbringing."

"Yes, it is sad. Now, if we had a dictator among our own people, to adjust the education laws and make it a criminal offence——"

"To spend so much on foreign education for one's daughters that nobody believes there can be any left for a dowry?"

If a dove had suddenly hissed like a snake, we could not have been more astonished. For it was Madame Akim who spoke. Angrily twisting her little hands together, and darting fiery glances towards the two men, the young and the middle-aged, so obviously discussing something together.

Akim Beg looked at his watch. Then he said with dignity, "It grows late. We must not keep our friends sitting here while the night dews fall."

They had not yet fallen, but certainly it was cooler. A little breeze, hardly more than a breath of air, was stirring the river. It would have stirred the willows too, but they were too weighted down with scarves and jackets to move.

13

As autumn approached, we could drive out and explore the country-side a little earlier, not waiting for evening now, because the strength of the sun was no longer dangerous. The curving, stony Bosnian roads led to many fantastic places among the hills. Brigandage had been put down, but they pointed out to me gaping holes in the rocks, where armed men had, not so long ago, made travelling a dangerous luxury.

It was a region rich in mineral springs and curative mud. Down in little pockets of the hills lay tiny spas frequented by visitors from all parts of Yugoslavia and sometimes from beyond. Cures for rheumatism were quite striking, so I was told. But one had to be pretty hardy in order to endure the local discomforts while taking them.

Nothing that could be called an hotel could be found in the primitive spas lying around Travnik. There were no flower-beds, nor little bands playing in the afternoons. But rooms, very simply furnished, could be rented in one or two rambling wooden houses built for the purpose of accommodating guests. And the baths themselves were mostly squares of cemented flooring into which the medicated waters were led by pipes. They were walled in but roofless, open to air and sunlight. The patients would use the bath communally, dressing and undressing on its verge, and leaving their clothes on the benches round about.

During our drives, I would notice men working in gangs on the roads. As I had heard much elsewhere about the Turkish distaste for hard labour, I was surprised to see that so many of them were wearing the fez. But Mr Meissner told me that he, as well as most other contractors, preferred to employ Turkish labour, finding the men more hard-working and less liable to take naps in the middle of the road than their Slav brothers.

There were other things that surprised me too. One morning we stopped in to pay a call on the wife of a builder to whom (as Mr Meissner had told me) the town fathers of Travnik had just given a big contract. The yard in front of his house was filled with squatting groups of Turkish roadmen. There they sat, idle, in the middle of a working day. One group had made coffee on a little fire of sticks lit right before the front door. Almost all the men were smoking and keeping their eyes fixed wistfully upon the curtained windows of the house, as if hoping for something to appear there.

The builder's wife bade me welcome in a few phrases of broken French, then burst into a spate of Serb which she addressed to Mrs Meissner. They both kept glancing out of the window. I guessed that they were discussing the curious behaviour of the workmen down in the courtyard beneath, and I asked Mrs Meissner for the explanation.

"They look so patient," I said, "almost as though they are rooted to the cobbles like plants."

"It is the patience of extreme poverty," she told me. "This is the end of the week. They should be off home today to their mountain villages with their wages in their hands after three weeks of hard work in the town. But they have no wages. They haven't been paid a penny. And they are afraid to return home to their families without them."

The conversation seemed an embarrassing one in the presence of the builder's wife. But she only nodded and smiled as if she could guess what was being said and approved of the clear way Mrs Meissner was saying it. The builder himself was of Austrian extraction, like Mr Meissner, and, like him, had appeared to inherit that sense of responsibility which still remains with the citizen of a great and civilized Empire, even after that Empire has fallen.

So I was puzzled. But as nothing in the atmosphere forbade my inquiring further, I said hesitatingly in English, "But—the builder? Where is he? Why hasn't he paid them?"

"Because he hasn't been paid himself. It was a town contract. The town was to pay him the lump sum agreed on for the whole work, and that included the men's wages. He has applied for that sum twice. The work was finished on Wednesday. Meanwhile he has been obliged to go to Belgrade on business, but before he went he was promised that during his absence the men at least would be paid. Without fail, he was told, by the end of the week. And look at them! They haven't received a ha'penny."

I took a step towards the window and looked at them. "Why are they waiting here, then? Don't they know their employer is away from home? And, whether he gets his money or not, why doesn't he pay them, anyway?"

But Mrs Meissner shook her head. "If he did that, the bill would never be paid at all. These men sitting down there are exerting a sort of moral pressure on the town. They are making the town councillors lose face. And the treasury may really be empty. The old civic traditions were overturned because they came from Austria. The new officials just don't know how to administer other people's money. They spend wildly, and then have nothing left with which to pay their debts."

I took another look out of the window and still persisted. "But if they *know* the builder isn't here, and can't come out and speak to them——"

"Oh, they know. His wife told them. And they know that it is the town that should pay them and not the builder. They aren't angry with him. But they've no one else to plead their cause, and perhaps they think that if they sit long enough in front of his house, he may drop down from heaven."

Two young boys sitting cross-legged just under the window swung round on their haunches to peer up at us. Flip-flap went the greasy cards on the cobbles, as a group of elderly workmen squatted, playing Török. The sun, now directly overhead, blazed with almost unendurable heat upon the front of the house.

The builder's wife now moved forward beside us. She stared down into the yard. Then she leaned over the window-sill, stretched her arm out and pulled to the heavy green shutters to keep out the glare. The sound of their closing reverberated with an iron clash into the air outside. It was followed, like a series of echoes, by the more distant closing of the shutters all round the house. And presently the white house itself seemed to have shut its eyes against the sight in the courtyard below. ...

Meanwhile our hostess had brought us the usual refreshment for callers in these parts—a glass of cold spring water and a saucer of roseleaf jam. She then got out a wooden box intricately carved, and showed us her collection of old embroideries. Nowadays the museums had started collecting peasant costume, but few costumes came into the market anyway, being handed down from mother to daughter. Even a scrap of fine needlework had become precious; and we were proudly shown a whole sleeve embroidered in threads of pure silver, and a baby's cap exquisitely worked. So, in the shaded, half-darkened room, we amused ourselves until it was time to go. But when we emerged into the fierce sunshine and crossed the courtyard again, we had to step over the sleeping forms of the men who had finished drinking coffee and playing cards, and were taking their siesta there on the stones.

Later, I heard what had happened when the builder returned at last from Belgrade. Deciding that it was hopeless to refer to the town any more for his just payment, and that to pay the men himself out of his own purse would establish a bad precedent, he told the foreman to have him arrested for non-payment of wages.

The foreman was startled. At first he refused. He said (in effect) that it was not the builder's fault that their wages were in arrears. It was the town's duty to pay them. But the builder insisted. So the foreman laid a complaint before the Chief of Police, who summoned the builder and asked him for an explanation as to why no wages had been paid. "It's not my fault," said the builder. And showed the Chief of Police his signed contract with the authorities of the town.

In Yugoslavia, as in most Balkan countries, the police authority was greater than that of the local town government. There was often, besides, much friction between the two departments. Had the builder gone to the police in the first place, he might have obtained satisfaction, but it is sure that no other town contract would ever have come his way. But since his own foreman had threatened him with arrest, who could blame him for answering the questions asked by the Chief of Police?

The latter was delighted to have an excuse for hauling the town authorities over the coals. An order was issued, commanding the town to pay its debt at once. Somehow or other the money was found and paid over. And the men departed for their hill-villages with their wages safe in their pockets.

I thought of Travnik's fertile soil, of its many tanneries and little businesses, and asked if the taxes yielded were really not sufficient to keep the roads in order and the essential services going?

"Of course. Only—you see, the councillors here are simple men. They don't mean to rob the town, but they aren't accustomed to controlling funds for the general use of the community. They only know there is a large sum of money lying in the bank, to which they have access. If one or other of them wishes to take his wife for a trip to Belgrade, he sees no reason why he should not help himself. And so, when the bills come in——"

And that (as her husband would say) was what came of an honest, hard-working peasant tucking his shirt into his trousers and going to work in an office instead of the fields.

14

In all hot countries one comes alive only towards evening.

The hills round Travnik boasted no woods, no fresh green patches to enliven the eyes during the day. Only when the sun began to go down behind them and the sky turn pink did they appear to bloom, and then it was with the copper reflection of a tiger-lily. Then, too, life began to show on them. Their sides were scarred white with many goat tracks running up the slopes towards some grassy plateau which yielded a little fodder, or under an overhanging rock that gave shade in the day-time. The nearest hill to us was crowned with the ruins of an old Turkish fort. Even during the midday heat, its arched recesses gave shade to a picnic party; but few travelled up through the glare until later in the day. Towards evening, however, the tracks leading towards it suddenly blossomed into colour, as little parties of Moslem women, dressed in their gay prints, could be seen at a distance scrambling up the hillside, bent on their evening coffee party.

It was the only opportunity they had for free social intercourse outside their own courtyards. The last remnants of harem tradition forbade their running in to one another's houses as the Christian women did, for fear they might come face to face with the men of the household. But for one magic hour before the sun set, the world was theirs. The men of Travnik were then safely indoors, and, by local custom, would stay there until their women had returned.

Myself being a woman, I was free to stray down the streets of the Moslem quarter at that hour. It was the only time I could get a glimpse of what lay behind those high white walls. Then the doorways would unlatch, and I would see for a moment the courtyards beyond, courtyards full of flowering shrubs and great, waxy magnolias. Out into the lane would step the women of the houses, moving the folds of stuff about their trousered legs ungracefully as they carried their watering-pots towards the nearest well.

Those pots, of dull pewter-coloured metal, had high, curved, delicate spouts and were enriched with fine threads of black inlay. They were easily the most beautiful things in the bare, scrubbed homes of the ordinary Moslem families. The tinsmith down in the bazaar hammered them out by the dozen, sitting cross-legged inside his little booth.

The women could therefore make their assignations by the water-trough, meeting there, chattering and giggling with their yashmaks up, because no honourable man would come out into the streets at the time of getting in the water supply. They would part finally, going each one back into her own house, to reappear again in a few minutes, now that the last task of the day was done. This time, as they passed me, they would be carrying baskets, and I would hear the chink of tiny coffee-cups and brass-handled coffee-pots being brought out to make their evening brew.

Quietly they threaded their way out of the town, picking up another friend or two as they went. But once the town was left behind I would notice, as I strolled after them in the same direction, how they dropped their swathed stolidity, and began to chase one another up the bare hillside, squeaking with laughter.

Then they would squat down in little groups under the shadow of the ruined fort. Their pink, blue, yellow trousers glittered like scraps of mosaic against the stones turned copper by the setting sun. If I walked past them, I could see the coffee-pot balanced upon a few smouldering sticks and smell the fragrance of the coffee. I could watch, passing from hand to hand, the progress of their delicious pastries, paper-thin and stuffed with meat or honey. But if Mr Meissner happened to accompany me, and their hands were too full of foodstuffs to adjust their yashmaks, they would turn round with the concerted motion of a Victorian family at prayers, and present large cretonne-covered behinds, so that the hillside seemed

suddenly to have put forth a crop of plump, vivid toadstools for
our admiration.

The Slav Christians of Travnik had another way of cele-
brating that sweet, cool period before the sun finally sank and
the Corso hour woke up its streets again. I walked right out of
the town one late afternoon, and across some fields, reaped
earlier in the season and now dark brown stubble. The fields
rose before me to form the crest of a hill. And right along the
ridge, against the skyline, I saw a party of young men and girls
dancing their national dance, the Kola.

They danced hand in hand in one straight line, slowly, with
dignity, to the harsh twanged music of the Serb gusla, a sort of
two-stringed fiddle plucked by hand. They appeared mere
colourless silhouettes against the bright sky behind them, like
the bas-relief on some piece of ancient pottery. The gusla music,
so ludicrous and tuneless when listened to indoors, seemed like
the piping of a strange sea-bird flown inland to set this lovely
picture in motion.

The town, the hills, the whole world was behind me, and
before me, only this simple drawing in black and rose, the line
of the ridge with the long grasses stirring in the evening wind
between the feet of the dancers, their outstretched arms cutting
across the rosy sky in one long wavering line, and the stringed
notes, archaic and unmusical, to which they danced.

Nearer the town there lay a deep, small gorge into which
the blue waters fell, to form a pool at the bottom. The stream
which formed the waterfall had passed in its course through
some mineral deposits higher up the valley, dyeing its waters a
deep indigo blue. A fringe of ferns and greenery had sprouted
round the edge of the falls, and in the sunshine the water cut
through them in an arc of sapphire. Even at noon, however,
the light was subdued by the high rocks on either side, and the
green of the fern fronds, the blue of the water, turned this place
into a stained-glass world.

Overhanging the gorge, protected from it only by a rickety
fence, was the little garden surrounding the Cuckoo Kafana.
This was a favourite café of the Moslems, who again seemed

to seek their relaxation in the shadow of the dead. For, behind the Kafana itself, sloping away from the gorge, lay the Turkish burying-ground, with its neglected tombs slanting sideways, their tops decorated with knobs sculptured like stone turbans. Some of the stones had sunk deep into the ground, some leaned towards one another as though in eternal, whispered conversation interrupted only by the sound of the blue waters falling into the pool.

Sometimes, to vary the Corso ritual and to get away from the noise and the dust of the town, we would drive out to the Cuckoo Kafana instead. The Meissners' old-fashioned victoria with its plodding horse would skirt the Blue Gorge at that time of evening when its sapphire colour had dulled, and when the orange lanterns of the Kafana above it were beginning to shine through the dusk. We would push our way upwards by a path leading between prickly thorns and damp, soft ferns. And we would order our coffee in the Kafana itself, rather than drink it in the equally damp little garden outside. We did not care about its view of dreary, gossiping gravestones, nor about the wet mist which rose up from the gorge to wreath itself round the tombs and then extend, in thin white spirals, towards the ruined fort higher up.

Inside, the Kafana was full of cheerful colour. The stove in one corner glowed dully with charcoal, and a row of brass-handled coffee utensils hung from the rack above. The wooden tables and benches looked reasonably well scrubbed. I can remember how, as I stepped into the room for the first time, the tapping of a lime tree against the window, the glimpse of gravestones through it, and the white mist blown across it accentuated the warmth and comfort of the room itself.

And then an incongruous sound had broken the stillness sharply. The sound, with all its Western associations, momentarily blew away the Oriental atmosphere about me as the mist outside was momentarily dispersed. It brought up memories of deep Bavarian forests, of Swiss souvenir shops, of tourist trophies brought home triumphantly. It was the note of a cuckoo clock proclaiming the hour.

Considering the name of the Kafana, I don't know why I should have been surprised. But there was the clock, sticking out from the wall, looking unbelievably foreign and out of place. Its carved oak leaves, its swaying pendulum shaped like an acorn, had so obviously been fashioned by a gentler civilization. Its hurried ticking accentuated the Eastern air of stately timelessness around me.

How had it found its way here, so far from the tourist centres of Europe? The proprietor answered that question for us as he brought us our coffee and slabs of sweetmeats. The Meissners translated as he went along. The clock? I noticed him glance at it meditatively as he spoke.

It had been a present given long ago, before the war, to the daughter of the last owner of the Kafana. It had been given to her by one of the Archdukes, a relative of the Emperor himself. The young Archduke was stationed here in Bosnia with his regiment. The girl was beautiful, and the two fell in love. He would ride down by the gorge, and she would steal out of the house to meet him there. No matter how her father strove to keep her in, she would find her way out of the house like a cat. . . .

A gust of wind drove the branch of the lime tree against the window again. The crazy wooden building creaked, as it must have done when the girl stole downstairs and out of it to meet her lover. She was a Moslem, so she would be wearing the wide, shapeless trousers gathered around her waist by an embroidered belt, and her eyes would be veiled by the square of net, until she reached him at least. If it was summer, then the gorge outside would be still and windless, an emerald and sapphire tent for their love. And if the sky still showed pink, the stillness would be broken by that faint call to conscience sounding from the minarets of Travnik; that call which echoed through the valley as the sun sank, indifferent to life or death or passion. . . .

No doubt she was a pleasant change for the Archduke; an interesting contrast between the blonde dancers of Vienna and this veiled young girl. No Austrian officer liked being posted to the utmost confines of the Empire. Anywhere outside of

Vienna was conducive to ennui. And Bosnia especially, where time stood still and the days were punctuated only by bugle calls from the barracks or the Hodja's call to prayer; Bosnia was reckoned a sort of punishment, and used as such for Archdukes and others who had misbehaved themselves.

However, sooner or later would come the recall to civilization. In the Archduke's case (the proprietor was saying) he behaved with generosity. He asked the girl to say what she would like him to send her from Vienna as a parting gift. But the girl had made a foolish choice. She might have asked for a piece of jewellery, or for something in gold, so that her own value might be enhanced in the marriage market. Indeed, without some such inducement she was not likely to find a husband at all. Women, however, are like children. They are amused by toys. The Archduke had once shown her a picture in a magazine of a little house carved out of wood, from which a bird sprang, shouting out the hour. So she asked him for one of these.

As soon as the Archduke got back to Austria, he sent her the clock. No doubt it had been made by one of his own foresters in the depths of some royal hunting-ground. It had hung on the wall ever since, the present proprietor having bought it in from the former one, along with the other fittings of the Kafana. It was, of course, a great curiosity in these parts, and was useful in attracting custom.

"What happened to the girl?" I asked.

The proprietor shrugged his shoulders. "She found no husband, of course. What could one expect, with the story so well known? But I kept her on in the kitchen, after her father died. Her pastry was paper-fine. Now she has grown so old; she forgets everything and is only fit to gather sticks."

It was not that night, however, but on a later one, that the old woman crossed the window outside, and then entered the room, bent almost double from age as well as the weight of the faggot of sticks on her back. The best place for gathering sticks was at the bottom of the gorge, for there the young trees cast down twigs and branches snapped off by the wind above. As she shuffled past our table, I looked up quickly, struck by a thought. Her wide pantaloons made a grotesque figure of her, and her eyes had sunk in her head till they seemed like little dead coals.

Just before reaching the kitchen she paused to loosen the bundle of faggots, easing it off her back on to the floor. Even without the heavy bundle, she remained bent almost double. Her weak arms let it down too suddenly, and the bit of cord twisted round it burst, scattering the pieces of wood all over the floor. Almost at the same moment the little door of the cuckoo clock flew open and the bird flapped its wings, shouting the hour. But the old woman paid no attention; she was too busy picking up the sticks strewn round about her feet.

15

Now that high summer was passing, the stalls in the Travnik bazaar began to be piled with mounds of fruit and vegetables. Melons lay cut invitingly open to show the pink flesh, or were sold by the slice for the immediate slaking of thirst. And the housewives all became frantically busy preserving as much as they could, to see them through the winter.

Here, in the heart of Bosnia, where almost no products other than local were consumed at the best of times, one had to rely, in winter, upon what one had in the house. The bitter climate with its frost and snow turned the ground to iron and killed all growing things in it. So there was a run upon everything useful for bottling. The trestles of the bazaar were piled high, every morning, with a special kind of small, sweet tomato, which was bought up at once. They were put into cauldrons and boiled for hours, being reduced to a highly concentrated pulp. This was poured into jars, sealed, and kept to make sauces or flavour stews.

The women of Travnik had learned something from the short Austrian occupation. They had learned the virtues of sauerkraut. They dug up their cabbages or bought them from the bazaar, chopped them and packed them in layers in barrels, sprinkling coarse salt over each layer. With tomato pulp, sauerkraut, and a few withered apples picked from their own trees and spaced out carefully on the storeroom shelves, they could at least diversify the winter menu of mutton and pastries.

I was helping Mrs Meissner with these preparations when we were interrupted by a neighbour who rushed in, breathless. "The Circus Assam is here!" she cried. "They've encamped in the field near the market this time. They will give a performance tonight!"

Throughout Central Europe and the Balkans, small, shabby

troupes of circus players wandered from village to village, crossing frontiers more frequently than travelled diplomats, and bringing the caperings of Punchinello to audiences simpleminded enough to enjoy them. For obvious reasons, the circus season was the summer. The extreme cold would make caravan living impossible in winter, and in the Balkans, at any rate, the primitive roads would be impassable for months.

It was a mystery how such small strolling companies managed to live during the winter months, and a mystery, too, where they lived. The Meissners and I had been discussing that very point the night before. For, as it happened, we had witnessed the entrance of the Circus Assam into Travnik, and that had led to idle speculations about what they did with themselves once the summer season was over. Their performances were too crude to enable them to obtain café engagements in the bigger cities. Mr Meissner had suggested that they and the flies went into hiding together.

Wherever they went, they had to stay until spring came, the snows melted, and the roads were dry again. Mr Meissner also pointed out that the name, Assam, was a slightly Slavicized form of Hassan, and so had been chosen to appeal to Mohammedan and Christian audiences alike. Probably, therefore, this particular little circus kept to an allotted territory with that admixture of population.

What language did they crack their jokes in? A sort of bastard German, I was told. It was the chief legacy left over from the days of the Austrian Empire which everyone still had in common. Impossible to guess, however, to what nationality the members of the troupe belonged. They seemed the offscourings of many countries and races. Coming home from an evening stroll, we had watched the two caravans lumber over the old stone bridge leading into the town. The first was driven by a man wearing a sheepskin coat and an air of authority; probably the owner in person. As it passed us, the curtain over the rear was twitched back, and an enormously fat woman peered out. She stared at us indifferently, then let the curtain fall back into place.

The second caravan was driven by a powerful-looking young Serb. He would be useful at pitching the tents and maybe doing the strong-man stuff, Mr Meissner said, eyeing him carefully. I was more interested in the two children, boy and girl, who sat one on each side of him. Before us, they had the still, aloof air of the artist who is not prepared to give anything away without being paid for it. The curtain which hung over the back of the cart was already drawn back. Sitting facing the road on an upturned box was a young girl. She was sewing white cuffs on to the dress laid over her knees. Her head was bent over her work; one could see the smooth hair parting and the blue-black coils of plaits over each ear. Whether from coquetry or because she was busy, she did not look up. And her waggon followed the other, over the bridge and into the town.

Though late in the season, it could still be blazingly hot. No one saw anything of the new arrivals during the heat of the day, when most citizens wealthy enough to invest in tickets for the circus would be within doors, anyway. But when it drew near to the hour of the Corso; when a slight coolness stole into the air, and people ventured out on the roads to greet one another and do some last-minute shopping—that was the moment chosen by the Circus Assam to draw attention to its existence.

Mrs Meissner and I, returning from a late sortie to the bazaar in search of a few pounds more of the little tomatoes, heard the hubbub come faintly towards us and waited at the corner of the street. Round it presently came the larger of the two circus waggons. Its top had been taken off to give a full view of the interior, and the horses drawing it now wore plumed, nodding headdresses. Close to the wheels ran all the little boys in Travnik, while a crowd of young men jostled each other, laughing and shouting, following the procession through the town.

The proprietor stood upright, banging a big drum. He had discarded his sheepskin and wore a shiny tail-coat and an old silk hat placed rakishly on the side of his head. Beside him, the Serb, now a grotesque and clownish figure, white-faced, scarlet-mouthed, played forlornly upon a saxophone. Balanced on opposite sides of the waggon stood the boy and girl, dressed as Cossacks, brave in polished boots. But it was the young girl with the smooth hair who was driving. A paste star trembled above her hair, and her spangled *tutu* showed a pair of thin and stringy legs, like those of an elderly chicken clad in pink tights.

It was almost dark, and the naphtha flares inside the wooden booths lining the main street had been lit. Here the procession paused. Turkish women shopping at the booths turned round to lift their veils a fraction momentarily, and peep at the curious sight. Men who had been seated outside the cafés ever since the sun began to go down, now rose and sauntered down the street to get a better view.

The man with the drum beat steadily until he judged the audience was complete. Then he stopped, and, making a megaphone of his hands, began to shout. "The Circus Assam, famous from Vienna to Stamboul, is here! Come tonight and see the Cossack Twins in their spectacular act! . . . The Wonderful Waltzing Mare . . . Mademoiselle Astra, Star of the Balkans, breathtaking Tight-rope Dancer!"

The windows all around us flew open. Women, veiled or unveiled according to their race, poked their heads out. They rested their elbows on the window cushions and stared down avidly at the cart. When the big man had finished his announcement, he seized the drumsticks again and gave a triumphant roll. Mademoiselle Astra braced her soiled white ballet shoes against the board, jerked at the reins, and the plumed horses moved forward again. The two children, one on either side of the cart, broke into a travesty of a Cossack dance, kicking and shuffling unsteadily, with white faces and anxious eyes upon the level of the road.

We went home and had supper. There was no hurry, I was informed. East of Vienna everything begins late, and if the circus was scheduled to start at eight-thirty, it would not begin till nine at earliest. We ate a leisurely supper, then went through the heavy carved gates into the lane which ran down to the town. The moon had risen, whitening the high walls on either side. And before we reached the end of the lane we could hear the beat of the big drum far in the distance.

Everyone was hurrying through the town towards the fields beyond. There, at the entrance to one of them, a small turnstile had been set up. Above it shone a makeshift little arch strung with electric bulbs. Beside it, on an upturned box, sat the fat, yellowish woman dealing out tickets. She marked each ticket with blue chalk as she handed it over. We pushed through the turnstile and entered the circus ground.

One ragged circular tent had been pegged down in the middle of the field. From the darkness on the other side of the tent we could hear the restless movement of animals; could catch a glimpse, as we walked towards it, of a plume, dyed baby blue, nodding coquettishly round a corner of the canvas as its wearer pawed the trodden grass, apparently anxious to have the equestrian turn well over.

Mademoiselle Astra came forward to take our tickets. She had scrambled out of her dancer's dress, and wore, for the moment, a shiny, tight-waisted jacket and skirt. She carried a tray of sweetmeats and cigarettes supported from one shoulder by a thick leather strap, and she paused only to check us in before crying her wares again, in a hoarse, raucous voice with no youth left in it.

There was a ring inside the tent, and one flaring bluish light high in the roof. As befitted our superior position in the town, we had been given tickets for the lowest circle of seats, in close proximity to grease-paint and flying hooves. The rest of the élite included the commanding officer from the barracks with his wife and children, the principal grocer (a man of wealth and substance), Akim Beg with his two daughters, and the Chief of Police with his family.

Immediately behind, with their knees pressing sharply into our backs, sat the smaller shopkeepers, the Croat farmer with Jusef Hassanovic next to him, Mustafa, the proprietor of the Turkish Garden, with his friend who kept the Cuckoo Kafana, and some families who had come down from the hills for the great occasion. Standing in a ring at the back of the tent, leaning against it so that the canvas bulged outwards in curious shapes, the young men of Travnik stood watching. And cluttering up the entrance like a bunch of agitated fowls were the veiled, trousered figures of such of the Mohammedan women as had been permitted by their men, not to sit beside them, but to hover on the outskirts of the entertainment, so as to hear and sense what they might of it through the stifling closeness of those squares of net which rose and fell with their excited breathing.

The flaring light above showed up the figure of the proprietor, now acting ringmaster in his dashing breeches, cutaway coat and dented silk hat. He cracked his whip twice. The Cossack Twins made an undignified entrance by burrowing through the foot of the tent and sprang, with a grotesque simulation of stage effrontery, into the middle of the ring.

They began their dance. Its music was provided by the Serb handyman who sat beside the big drum in his shirt-sleeves, playing his saxophone for a bar or two, then dropping it and taking a turn on the drum. The girl stuck her hands out behind her ears, waggling hands and head together while her legs kicked wildly here and there. The boy squatted on his haunches, shooting out a pair of high-heeled Cossack boots in fevered rhythm whenever the drum superseded the saxophone.

They must have been hard at work since their arrival, doing odd jobs about the camp. Their eyes glittered with fatigue, and the dark blue circles round them showed up as clearly as if they had been painted there. Yet if their antics faltered one moment, it seemed to me that the ringmaster's whip no longer cracked harmlessly in the air but curled about their ankles, spurring them on to more frantic effort.

Mrs Meissner saw my distress. "I dare say they've put the poor little things on first to get them out of the way," she whispered soothingly, "and then they can creep off to bed."

The ring was suddenly empty again. The ringmaster walked backwards towards an opening in the tent, and received from an unseen hand a heavy iron chain. He pulled it, cracking his whip once more. A small, moth-eaten bear shambled sullenly in, and surveyed us with red-rimmed eyes.

"They find them up here in the mountains," Mrs Meissner said in my ear. "Sometimes a gypsy will train one to tramp up and down a man's body. It is good for rheumatism, like massage. Often I have come on an old peasant lying down on the road and a bear dancing on top of him, kneading at his rheumatism in return for a trifle of money."

The saxophone was silent now. Only the drum beat ominously. Slowly, in time to the sullen noise, the bear lifted one hind leg, then the other, standing upright meanwhile, swaying a little from side to side, so that its shadow, shooting up gigantically against the back wall of the tent, seemed to embrace the whole audience in its paws. I watched, fascinated, that great shadow which seemed to have no relation to the small, grotesque object swaying angrily in the middle of the ring. Then all at once the shadow vanished. The shambling creature had fallen on all fours again and was being hustled out of sight, to make way for a human performer no less grotesque.

Now the drum was being played by the ringmaster himself. He must have taken over that duty some minutes before, to allow the Serb to slide unobtrusively out of the way. Somewhere behind the tent, the Serb had scrambled into his wide, checked pantaloons, had fixed his red, matted wig in place, and had smeared his face with the traditional red and white of the clown. And there he was, smiling and bowing right under the light in the roof of the tent.

A little ripple of attention passed over the audience. The young men at the back straightened up suddenly against the canvas walls. They stopped cracking open the monkey-nuts bought from Mademoiselle Astra with which they had been beguiling the duller part of the programme. They began to guffaw delightedly at the clown's wit, which was of the primeval type that slides and sits down suddenly on the greasy trodden grass of the ring; that leaps to evade the ring-master's whip; that stops dead under the light to turn its awful, masklike face slowly from one member of the audience to another.

But perhaps I did him an injustice, for I could not under-stand the remarks he shot out now and then. They seemed to be in an odd parrot-mixture of German, Serb, and a few Turkish words thrown in here and there. Perhaps it was their very unintelligibility which delighted the audience, who rocked with laughter. And it was in a blaze of warm success that the clown took his last tumble backwards towards the main exit, scattering the Turkish women, who gave squeaks of fright and pleasure as he crashed through them and rolled out into the night.

A pause followed, in which the drum and the saxophone were played alternately by the ringmaster, sounding like two fantastic creatures, male and female, answering one another. People grew restless. They turned round to summon the girl with the sweetmeat tray, and then noticed for the first time that she had disappeared.

Suddenly there was a clattering sound of hooves, and the two bony caravan horses, now streaming with coloured plumes and jangling with bells, ambled into the ring, encouraged by the ringmaster's whip into showing a clumsy travesty of spirit. Their meek eyes rolled about the audience, as though apologiz-ing for this metamorphosis, which was no stranger than the one which had overtaken Mademoiselle Astra herself.

For now, as she thundered past with a muscular foot on the back of each horse, she was wearing the tulle skirt of glamour again. A layer of grease-paint had softened the premature sharpness of her features, bringing back youth and pretti-ness again. And the great paste star on her forehead, catching the light above, glittered as bravely as though it remained for ever on top of the horizon, instead of shining only for a few brief moments before tomorrow's daylight would show up its tawdriness again.

So the circus managed to end in a blaze of excitement and glory. I was in two minds about going to see the encampment next morning, lest its pathetic shabbiness should be once more, painfully, in evidence. But when next morning came, the field was empty again. Nothing remained of Travnik's strange visitors but a few coloured wisps of paper blowing against the fence.

"Where have they gone?" Mr Meissner repeated my question. "Westwards, always westwards, towards Czechoslovakia."

"I should like, some day, to go back to Czechoslovakia myself," I said thoughtfully.

An unwonted touch of grimness came into his good-humoured face. "Then you'd better hurry. It's not going to hold together for long."

By now I was used to such remarks made about the Succession States by disgruntled members of the Old Empire. "You only say that because you're an Austrian," I answered hotly.

He shrugged his shoulders. "I'm a realist. If you take the train, you may get there in time. I doubt if the caravan will."

Part Four

THE GREEN FEATHER

16

I WAS in the train again, but not bound for Czechoslovakia. As it happened, I was in the wrong train, anyway. I had rashly got out at Mostar in my way from Travnik to the Dalmatian coast. That was at four o'clock in the morning, but the carriage was so crowded I had been unable to sleep. The next morning, at the same unearthly hour, I impressed on the porter at Mostar station that he must find me an emptier carriage when the Dalmation express came in. Willing to oblige me, he had found me a corner seat in a portion of the express which did not happen to go by Dubrovnik. But naturally, I did not know that at the time.

It was very comfortable to have not only a corner but the whole side of one carriage to oneself. Opposite, each in another corner, slept a paunchy little commercial traveller and a young Serbian officer who spoke a few words of French. I woke to find the compartment bathed in a brilliant, diamond-hard light. The sunshine had another quality from that of the Bosnian hills. It seemed paler and lighter, and free from dust. And out of the window, in a long glittering strip, showed the sea.

The young officer woke up and yawned. He caught my eye and smiled. "Bonjour, Mademoiselle!"

I looked at my watch. It was half-past six. "When do we reach Dubrovnik?" I asked.

"Dubrovnik! But Mademoiselle should have changed trains two stations back! This portion goes to Herzegovina!"

There was a stunned silence, while the sea flickered indifferently by.

"This portion does not go *near* Dubrovnik!" the Serb said agitatedly in his broken French. "For the moment it is running along the coast. But it turns inland after the next station, and——"

"Hören-Sie!" the German commercial traveller burst out. "Get out at the next station, before the train leaves the coast! No other goes from it to Dubrovnik, I grant you; but there must be some sort of conveyance...."

The train was slowing already. Judging from the few houses about, it must have been only a "halt."

"Make haste!" The German had stood up; was handing down my luggage to the Serb who had already lowered the strap of the window. Past his head I saw a clean little station. A small motor-lorry stood close by the rails. Two porters were rolling out large milk-cans from the van.

The Serb shouted out to the porters. The porters shouted back. The door swung open, and I and my luggage were deposited on the bare earth beside the rails. The Serb called after me, "It is all arranged, Mademoiselle! That lorry is going to Dubrovnik with the mails and the milk. The driver says he will be enchanted to take you. Bon voyage!"

The train moved on and disappeared.

Someone had already grabbed my suitcases and put them into the lorry. We moved off through a landscape of twisted olive trees and flat-roofed houses, where melons lay ripening, down towards the sea.

I had never seen a landscape like this. With all my wanderings, I had never seen the south. The little houses, pink or white or yellow; the grotesque shadows cast by the olive trees, and all in morning sunshine as sharp and clear as a sword.

And there lay the Adriatic at our feet. Dubrovnik itself was out of sight. But a narrow stalk of land ran out into the sea, spreading mushroom-like into a yellow port. I could see the lagoon, and the campanile rising up from its edge. I pointed down questioningly.

"Cavtat," the driver said, showing all his teeth in a grin. "Si, si, Signora. Cavtat!"

Cavtat. I went over the syllables carefully in my mind. It looked beautiful. It looked cheap. I was going to stay there and not in Dubrovnik itself. I saw a little steamer leave the quay and pass, like an electric toy, behind the hill to our right. It reminded me of one of the tiny electric boats travelling eternally up and down the painted wall of the Haus Vaterland.

We rounded the hill and Cavtat disappeared, blotted out. Instead we were looking down on the walled city of Dubrovnik; Ragusa, as it was called before the war changed everything, including names. The town whose name was borrowed by the argosies which used to put in to this port, which in its heyday had rivalled Venice.

I could see a great cruise-ship lying at anchor. By the time we entered the narrow streets of the town, the tourists had come ashore and were pouring through them. For the first time in weeks I heard English spoken freely all about me. Young men in flannels drifted past, swinging cameras. Bunches of freckled girls in white tennis shoes and striped Macclesfield silk dresses giggled, staring about them. Their voices echoed through the shadowy arcades, wiping away the atmosphere as with a sponge. Even the Rector's Palace, even the great fountain, was not Dubrovnik's or mine. It was theirs.

I had breakfast, left my suitcases in the hotel, and went off to the travel bureau. Here at least was peace, with no animation whatever. The tourist industry had not yet been geared to the extent of animating the languid clerk behind the counter. He was busy manicuring his nails, and occasionally shouting a friendly word or two towards the typist in the inner office. I had met his kind all over the Balkans, and knew I could wait for ever unless his interest was aroused. But how to rouse it?

Meanwhile I asked diffidently if he had a list of hotels in Cavtat. He shook his head.

"No hotels," he said, busy with the nail-file.

I said that was a pity, because I had just arrived from Bosnia, and wished to stay in Cavtat above all other places. The file wavered. For a second he actually looked at me. I could see his eyes were black; not the sparkling black of the Latin, but the sleepy black of one who has a touch of Oriental blood in him. The look had come when I said Bosnia. One must make an opening when one can.

I leaned against the counter negligently, as if I had merely drifted in to make a little conversation. "Of course, Dalmatia is very beautiful," I said, "and it would be foolish not to see it now I'm here. But I must confess the charm of Bosnia quite captivated me."

There was no mistake. He dropped the nail-file entirely. "I am a Bosnian myself, Mademoiselle! From what part——"

"From Travnik."

"Travnik! I was born and spent my boyhood there."

I thought it time to make my social standing clear. "Then you will no doubt know Akim Beg? A delightful family!"

"A prince among men. Indeed yes. And Mademoiselle is a friend of the family? Any friend of Akim Beg is a friend of mine. Let me see, what was it Mademoiselle wished to know? I confess I was not giving my attention entirely——"

I told him again. He looked thoughtful.

"Cavtat is a very little place. Rather primitive. Here we have good hotels, running water, even hot and cold. I can find accommodation easily here. A word from me that accommodation for a friend is required, and the best suite in the best hotel will be Mademoiselle's."

That was neither what I wanted nor what I could pay for. I had taken a violent fancy to Cavtat, and at last he saw that nothing else would content me. To do him justice, I don't believe he was thinking of his rake-off from one of the local hotels. He was honestly thinking of my comfort and happiness now that he knew I liked Bosnia and was an acquaintance of Akim Beg.

"If Mademoiselle can give me time, say a few hours, I shall with great happiness inquire about rooms at Cavtat. The boat from there comes in at midday. I shall go down to the harbour and ask of those who are quitting it."

Outside the little office the sun had begun to blaze fiercely. I was tired. I went back to the hotel and waited there until after lunch. The foyer was cool and there was a good view of the street. Presently I saw the Bosnian clerk walking along it, making for the entrance.

Then a car passed, blotting him out for the moment. The

car pulled up with a jerk as if stopped by some object in the middle of the road. From behind the bonnet appeared the clerk. He must have leaped suddenly right into its way to stop it. Now he was hanging on to the handle of the door, his head inside, his other arm gesticulating emptily above the pavement. He seemed to be trying to persuade someone to leave the car.

A majestic elderly woman stepped out. Even at that distance one could see she was English, and of a type which was rapidly vanishing. She was tall and angular, and she had transformed her straw hat into a sort of solar topee with bands of green veiling swathed round its crown and falling down behind. The clerk had taken her arm now. He was urging her towards the hotel. Presently they entered and stood before me.

The Englishwoman surveyed me from top to toe. Then she said, "I think our friend must have gone out of his mind. He tells me you are English. Even so, why should we inflict ourselves upon one another?"

Her tone was cold. Evidently she did not like to be hustled. The clerk began to talk again, urgently, in either Serb or Croat. The lady in the green veil seemed to soften a little.

"You want to visit Cavtat? One can visit it agreeably in an afternoon, but few people wish to stay longer. My daughter lives there, as it happens. That is why he thought I might be of use to you."

A waiter was hovering round. I ordered coffee for three. The veiled woman and I probed each other gently, while the clerk rolled his dark eyes from one to the other, trying to follow from our tones the drift of the conversation. She turned out to be the widow of a Cambridge professor, whose only child had married a Serb. Because of that, she had uprooted herself from her proper setting and lived now in Dubrovnik to be near her daughter. But for all that she remained the wife of a Cambridge professor.

She made up her mind about me. "Sasha—my son-in-law— is taking the evening boat back to Cavtat. I will put you in his charge. There are one or two villas which take guests. I dare say he will know the most suitable."

The Bosnian clerk beamed his satisfaction when he heard that arrangements had been made. We shook hands warmly and he took his departure. Presently the Englishwoman took hers as well. She was now cordial but still outspoken. She had had quite a number of things to see to, when he had interrupted her schedule by forcibly removing her from her taxi. I apologized.

By evening it was not only cooler, it was very much quieter. The tourist hordes had returned to their cruise-ship and the residents of Dubrovnik now had the place to themselves. The great fountain of Onofrio was in shadow now. Its fourteen jets no longer sparkled, but fell with a dull splash into the basin beneath them. Women were hauling in their washing from the ropes they had slung across the street at sixth- or seventh-floor level; and the birds in their wicker cages sang shrilly, as if they knew that soon the sun would be sinking and darkness would make them mute.

I saw the green veil a long way off. It was down at the harbour, talking to a youngish man in tennis flannels. We were introduced. "This is my son-in-law, who is a writer too. He has been to Cambridge, so you won't have any difficulty about language."

Sasha still looked somewhat dazed by the sudden responsibility thrust upon him. But he got me and my suitcases on board the toy steamer, the one I must have looked down on from above in the early morning. It looked larger now, but not much. And the coast drew away from us in a rose-coloured haze, until presently the boat nosed towards the coastline again, and there was the narrow neck of land pushing out into the water before us and the tall Italianate tower by the quay.

As we drew alongside, I saw that the yellow flagstones of the quay were set with restaurant tables and iron chairs. "This is the only eating-place in Cavtat," Sasha informed me; adding, "The people who run it let out rooms in their villa up there. I think you had better stay with them."

I looked at up there. The harbour itself, with the church, the campanile, and a row of three rather pretentious villas, seemed to occupy all the flat ground in the isthmus. Above it, the rocky sides of the hills were cut into terraces, with stone steps leading steeply from one to the other. Along these terraces were strung out the rest of the houses of Cavtat. Big or small, they appeared to be balancing themselves like swallows' nests on the razor edge of each row. But in spite of that each had a pocket handkerchief of garden soil behind them, where the rocks had been further cut back and basketsful of earth deposited so that something might grow.

It was to one of those houses that Sasha had pointed. Once landed, he made the negotiations for me, said good-bye, and left me to follow the bandy-legged little waiter who spoke a few words of German and who had been ordered by his employer to carry my things up to the villa.

I climbed one of the rocky stairways behind him. By now the quick southern dark had almost fallen, and I was anxious to see my new surroundings before they were blotted out altogether. The house we entered was bare and sounding, like a box. It consisted entirely of rooms let out, with their keys, to visitors. Neither the hall nor the corridors had a stick of furniture in them; and there was no plumbing whatever.

But, as Sasha's wife told me afterwards, that was a good thing. Such out-of-the-way places lacked sanitary inspection, and hotel keepers were all too prone to bait their hotels with modern-looking fitments, while neglecting the question of proper drainage. At any rate, the Villa Epidaurus held no risk of typhoid, while its empty corridors, its sparsely furnished bedrooms, were kept reasonably clean.

Mine contained an iron bedstead, a wooden chair, a wash-stand with a tiny jug and basin, and some hooks behind the door. But when I looked out of the window I didn't care. The moon had risen, dazzlingly, to pick out the white roofs of the houses and reflect itself on the harbour water down below. Lights like fireflies shone along terraces of other houses hidden behind arbours of vines. And behind this house, almost on a level with the window out of which I was hanging, one brilliant arc light, suspended from a pole, lit up a little garden where an evening party was evidently taking place.

The garden itself was only a scooped-out shell of greenery under the overhanging rock. But five or six men and girls sat round a wooden table in the middle of it. One of the men had an accordion; another had a ringing tenor voice. The soft southern airs borrowed from Italy matched the moonlight, the scent of rosemary, and the glittering water of the bay.

I undressed and lay on my iron bedstead, listening. And then I fell asleep.

17

THE heart of the place was down by the harbour.

Those still waters, which mirrored the great yellow tower beside them, held a curious fascination for me, even before I heard what they were supposed to hide. It seems that the old Greek city of Epidaurus, birthplace and shrine of Æsculapius the God of Healing, had been destroyed farther up the Adriatic by some sort of cataclysm of war or nature. The survivors had fled here, to continue their worship of the god. But again nature had destroyed them. Their town had been engulfed by the sea, and now lay at our feet, fathoms deep under the greenish waters of the lagoon.

At least so people said. They said, too, that when a winter storm of unusual violence made the water boil up, one could hear the faint tone of a bell. For generations all the little boys of Cavtat must have amused themselves, as I saw them doing when out in a boat with their fathers. I would see them bend suddenly like small clasp-knives over the edge of the boat, oblivious to their parents' shouts and the dangerous tilt. If they were very small, their heels kicked in the air and their bullet heads almost touched the water, as they tried to catch a faint glimmer of the campanile which they were sure housed the bells down below. But only the reflection of the real one rippled up to them. And then their fathers jerked them back by the seat of their pants, and their roars of disappointment came right back to me where I stood.

At night one could watch the sardine-fishers sail out into the bay. There was a tinning factory higher up the coast, and most of the men of Cavtat made it their life's work to supply the factory. Once the little fleet had reached the deeper waters where the shoal swam, they separated and lay, with their oars shipped, rocking gently. They lay in pairs at a stated distance from each other, with a rope stretched between each pair of boats, and half-way down the rope was a lantern. The sardines, fascinated by the lights, would swim right up to them, to be enmeshed in the net spread under the water from boat to boat. It was like catching moths.

I got up very early one morning to see the boats come in. Even at dawn the landscape seemed suffused by a clearer light than in the misty atmosphere of the north. Everything, even the houses washed with pale colour, looked a delicate grey. The rock staircase was pearly grey under my feet, and the giant cacti lining the path down to the water-level were mere spikes of iron grey. But the world seemed still asleep, and no one moved along the rock terraces except myself.

Nobody was in sight until I got down almost to ground-level. Then a big bush of rosemary stirred beside me. Out from under its silvery leaves stole a cat. The cat did not waste a glance on me, but streaked down the remaining steps, apparently giving chase to another which had suddenly appeared before us both. I reached the last step of the stairway which let climbers down upon the yellow flagstones forming a narrow road between the three large villas and the water itself. The villas themselves were still shuttered. But cutting across their doorsteps, streaming down each of the other stone stairways leading from above, were cats, grey or black, piebald or tortoiseshell, all moving stealthily in the same direction, towards the anchorage in the lagoon.

The quay was a line of cats. Some moved about restlessly, mewing. Others sat stolidly, their tails gathered round them, staring out to sea. None of them paid the slightest attention to me as I stood behind them and stared in the same direction. We were all watching the approach of the sardine fleet, listening to the sound of the oars which echoed across the lagoon.

Now a pinkish light was creeping over the water. The sun appeared slowly over the horizon, catching the tower of the campanile first and warming its stones gradually downwards. Behind me, the three big villas were waking to life. I could hear their shutters being thrown back and hooked against the wall. The boats approached slowly, laden with their catch. One or two little boys had joined us on the quay, and, half turning, I could see the rustling white skirts of a few of the fishermen's wives making their way down to the water's level. They were beautiful, those women of the Dalmatian coast. They showed their Latin blood, with maybe a touch of the ancient Greek. They moved proudly, majestically forward to see what their men had brought.

The boats were made fast and the catch emptied out over the stones. Emptied and weighed and poured into sacks again, while the cats were chased off by little boys armed with stones. But enough small, squashed bodies were left on the quay to content the animals, accustomed for centuries to this breakfast routine. The smell of fish was still overpoweringly strong, and the stones under my feet were slippery with the pailsful of water thrown over to cleanse them before the iron tables and chairs of the restaurant could be put in place again.

Everyone melted away, even the cats. The sun had risen clear above the water-line, turning it into gold. But there was still some time to wait before I could get my coffee and rolls. I did not feel inclined to make the way upward again, to my bleak little room with the iron bedstead. Instead, I went into the old church beside the quay and sat down on a chair facing the altar.

It was a rough, plain little church. Its windows were of plain glass tinted yellowish, and there were the usual doll-like, simpering figures of saints with votive offerings before them. The temple of Æsculapius must have been much richer, more beautiful. Perhaps the descendants of the citizens of Epidaurus had got tired of beautifying shrines which, in the end, had failed to mollify the gods. But the strange thing about that church was, that on the stillest day a wind seemed to play around it.

The morning had been absolutely still. But as usual, as I sat there, I could hear it moaning and sobbing outside. The inside of the church was like the sea; eternally sounding to movement. The windows never ceased to rattle, and the old stone building seemed buffeted by some force seeking to get in. The Madonna smiled mawkishly, not even deigning to listen. And the gods that had been banished redoubled their fury, trying to gain entrance.

I felt hungry now. I pushed the heavy door open once more and stepped outside. Immediately the air was still again. Not one of the little shrubs about the door even stirred. It was warmer too. The sea had lost its pink stain and was now like a great, shining aquamarine. And the houses on the carved-out terraces above me had regained their colour; they stood out startlingly, blue and pink and yellow cubes against the rocks behind them.

A few people were down on the quay having breakfast already. Each of the little tables had its gay striped umbrella, and Franz the waiter was going from one to the next, wearing the shiny black alpaca jacket I think he slept in. He gave me the South German greeting, "Grüss Gott, Fräulein!" Then he brought me the invariable and rather unpalatable breakfast. A large white cup full of coffee with a little milk poured in and already formed into a skin, a thick slice of greyish bread in the saucer, a separate knife, and a pat of butter on a round glass plate.

"Grüss Gott!" called out the Czech family at the next table. They consisted of a father, mother, and daughter from Prague. All three were enormously fat, and I was not surprised to hear that they ran a Bier-Stube at home. The father sat in his shirt-sleeves, with his massive arms upon the table. The mother faced him looking like a jelly done up in a striped cotton frock. And Linda, the daughter, who might have been pretty if she had not had a double chin already, wore a round-necked dress that made her look like a bloated baby, and coquettish curls tied back with pale blue ribbon.

"Grüss Gott!" smiled the Viennese widow, sitting quietly at the next table. Old and unobtrusive though her clothes were, she exuded an air of chic so that one could almost tell at a glance the capital she came from. I had always noticed that with Viennese encountered on my travels. No matter how poor they were (and Cavtat was the holiday resort for those with slender purses), they managed somehow to look elegant. We had discussed the matter, she and I, one night when everyone else had gone for an evening sail to Dubrovnik and Franz had put us together at the same table.

It was, she said, merely the difference in aim between a middle-class Frenchwoman and a Viennese. The typical Viennese (she told me) aimed, like the British, at looking like a gentlewoman. A Frenchwoman of the same class would look either frumpish or coquette. But then (she shrugged her shoulders gently) the whole of Middle Europe took its tone in fashion from Vienna, not from Paris. Vienna had prided itself always upon evolving fashions to suit a race whose looks and lines were entirely different from the Latin.

"Of course," she said, "I don't include the international rich, who can afford to dress with individuality to suit their own particular type. The great dressmakers exist for them. They can command unique models because they can pay for them. There are only a few designers in the world who are able to turn out a truly original model without being bizarre. It makes no difference if the designers live in Rome, in Paris, or in Vienna. They do not reflect any nation. They reflect only themselves."

This morning the little Viennese was wearing, as usual, her well-cut, well-worn grey flannel suit. One could hardly tell how she varied it, but she did. By an exquisitely frilled blouse of lemon yellow one day and a lemon yellow beach-bag at her neat, black-sandalled feet. By dazzling white on Sundays or if she was going to Dubrovnik for the afternoon. By coral pink and a great coral-coloured sunshade.

She told me her husband had been killed in the war, and that she worked in a bank and lived at home with her parents. The suit, made by a good tailor in the Kartnerstrasse, had taken several months' salary to pay for. But it would wear, and look good, for several years. I should have liked to see what she did with it for an evening party. I felt sure she could so camouflage it that not a whisper of flannel would be heard.

The fourth table was occupied by a sea-captain recovering from a bout of pneumonia. He must have got his ticket very early, for he was still young and handsome. A Dalmatian by birth, he had chosen his own sea-coast on which to recuperate. Dark and melancholy, he sat almost all day writing letters at the little iron table, and avoiding the glance of the fat Czech girl at meals.

There was now some activity behind the sumptuous curtains of the largest of the three villas opposite; the one which belonged to a Yugoslav shipping magnate. He had evidently ordered his speed-boat round, much as one orders one's horse. The throb of its engines echoed loudly as it shot out from its boat-house and came to rest, rocking, beside his own landing-stage. One by one his beautiful daughters issued out of the house, evidently bound for Dubrovnik from the glittering display of the latest fashions. They cast amused glances at us sitting there, drinking coffee already poured out, without even plates before us to spread our hunks of bread on. Linda the Czech girl blushed and turned her head away. But the Viennese gazed calmly back, and then addressed me from the next table almost before they were out of earshot.

"I think one should dress according to one's surroundings," she remarked, "and not merely to mark one's wealth. But then, the newly-arrived always go in for display. Whether they are nations or individuals, it is the same."

As she spoke in German, the newly arrived members of the Czech and Yugoslav nations present on the quay understood her perfectly. And they obviously rejoiced that a member of the superior race had spoken for them all. Self-esteem flowed back into their faces. Questions of national prestige were all very well, and on another occasion they might have bitterly resented an Austrian's hit at the newness of their respective countries. But first came the fact that they, being all holiday-makers together, had been snubbed and ignored by a family rich enough to possess their own villa. No cheerful "Grüss Gott" or greeting in any other language ever issued from that purse-proud household. The Viennese woman had put it firmly in its place. They were grateful, and for the moment were prepared to overlook completely where she had come from herself.

Round the corner, just out of sight of the quay, was a narrow strip of shingle affording good bathing-ground. The Cambridge professor's daughter, along with her husband and children, passed on their way to it nearly every day. They would pause at my table, often with a bundle of books for me to read, and I would return the ones I had borrowed from them before. Sasha's wife was a pale, shy young woman with a distaste for small-talk or much social life. She belonged to an English university town just as clearly as did her mother. It came as a shock of surprise when I first heard her fluent Croat as she spoke to the sea-captain, and the equally fluent Italian—next most familiar language along that coast—with which she replied to a question asked by the Czechs.

Last of all, the postman strolled on to the quay. He had a grizzled moustache of the same cinnamon colour as the jacket he wore, a cool contraption of linen generally worn loose across his shoulders like a cloak. The only part of him that looked in the least official was his cap with its shiny peak. Perhaps he had a uniform but had decided it was too hot and too good for a place like Cavtat. Where he came from and where the letters were sorted, I never knew. I presume he troubled himself to climb up to the houses of the residents and deliver their mail in the usual way. I know that, with transients like myself, he saved himself trouble by handing us out our letters at meal-times as we sat on the quay.

There was an old piano which stood near the shed where Franz heated up the coffee and sliced the bread. The piano was used occasionally by a professional pianist who, with the rest of his dance-band, was fetched from Dubrovnik to provide music on special occasions. It was also used by the postman every day. As soon as he had slapped the last letter down on the last iron table, he would walk over to the piano and play us a tune. He vamped wildly, and it was nearly always the first few bars of "O Sole Mio!" This little interlude was meant to be funny. He would end with a sob and a gurgle in his throat, salute politely, and walk off the quay.

But this morning he was too interested in reading over my

shoulder the note he had just delivered to bother about the piano. It had not come through the post; he must have been given it direct, for he certainly knew who it was from. He informed everyone sitting around.

"From Her Excellency the widow of our late Prime Minister, Nicolai Pachitsh!" he informed them proudly.

Inside the envelope was the widow's calling-card. Across the top was written, "Hoping to have the pleasure of entertaining you at five o'clock this afternoon."

The captain strolled over from his table and looked at the card. From his travels he had picked up a little English, so he was able to translate the message for the benefit of the postman, who had been very annoyed to find it written in a language he could not read.

Having made his translation, he handed the card back to me. "The old lady is very hospitable. Hospitable, and perhaps a little bored with living in this backwater. Her husband was prime minister and faithful friend to King Peter, who ruled here during the war. What intrigues she must have taken part in then! Court life in the Balkans never lacked excitement or danger!"

There was no address on the card. I asked him where the old lady lived.

"Oh, I will take you there," he said at once. "I know the house well; I was made free of her Five O'clocks long ago. Nowadays any stranger is grist to her mill—even a British writer, or a poor sailor with a patch on his lung. We bring the world to her door."

18

On our way there the captain explained why this elderly rem-
nant of King Peter's court was to be found in a place like Cavtat. Her family had been prosperous wine-growers in the district.
She was brought up here, long ago. Then, along with her husband, she had been plunged into the tortuous politics round a
Balkan throne. Belgrade must have been an exciting place between the years 1912 and 1918. She had seen the small Kingdom of Servia suddenly enlarged and aggrandized by the acqui-
sition of former Italian, Austrian, and Hungarian territory.
Such were the rewards of choosing the winning side. And, one
must add in fairness, of Servia's fighting support of the Allies.

But Servia was now Serbia, merged in the new, sprawling
Kingdom of Yugoslavia. The old King was dead, and so was
his famous Minister. Madame Pachitsh, like the Emperor Dio-
cletian, shook off all greatness and retired to the coast of Dalmatia. She had made a charming home for herself (so the
captain told me as we walked towards it) out of an old store-
house quite near the quay. It had been left to her by her vine-
yard-owning father, and she had probably forgotten all about it
until she grew old. Now she had come back to live in the rooms
where his wines had been stored, above the vaults where they
had lain maturing.

There was room here for just a narrow strip of pavement,
with a few necessary shops, and, farther off, a very old, very
massive stone house. Unlike the villas on the other side of the
quay, there had been no attempt to beautify its outside by
coloured paint or shutters. Its lower story was obviously sunk
below the ground, for the upper halves of its windows appeared
at one's side, above the pavement and without any grilles or
iron railings to protect them. But the glass was so thick, it was
impossible to see through into the rooms beyond. We passed by

and reached the gate in the stone wall. The captain rang a bell and the gate was flung open.

The side of the house had risen up, rough-hewn and uncouth, straight from the road. But here was the hidden garden, where spikes of lilies rose up to the blue sky above, and a vine arbour, hanging already with tiny grapes. A manservant opened the door, and we were ushered down a short flight of stone steps, into what must have once been a vast wine-cellar or vault.

This vault was now the old lady's drawing-room, and deliciously cool after the enervating heat outside. The stone walls of the room had been smoothed and polished. The floor had been relaid with slabs of silver-grey marble. A few pieces of Empire furniture stood around, their gilding bringing warmth to the room. Curtains of plum-coloured silk were looped back from the windows whose upper halves we had passed on the street outside. And I could see now that the thick glass was greenish in tone, giving an under-water quality to the room.

An old lady rose from a Récamier sofa, coming forward with outstretched hands. An exquisite old lady with hair as carefully coiffed as though going to an audience with King Peter himself. "So kind!" she murmured. "So kind to come to see an old woman and bring her news from the outside world!"

The captain kissed her hand. She relapsed into French which both he and she knew better than English. The manservant brought in coffee and cakes. She conversed with ease and tact; with curiosity too, to know what was happening in Britain, and with (I sensed) a certain anxiety as to what might be happening in Germany at the moment. Listening to her, seeing the grace with which she offered her cups of pallid tea, one could not but think of the far road she had travelled from her girlhood as the daughter of a peasant-proprietor on the bleak slopes above Cavtat.

"But where is Macdougal?" she exclaimed suddenly. "I find myself with a Scottish guest for once in my life, and Macdougal not here to enjoy her! Nor the tea, which is getting cold. . . ."

"Miss Macdougal was governess in Madame's family," the captain explained in a low voice, "and she still makes her home here. It must be so long since she left your country, naturally she has more interest in this house now than in anything else."

A few minutes later, Miss Macdougal slid silently into the room. All her movements were silent, even subservient. As subserviency is not a quality of my race, I put it down to her lengthy existence as a dependant. But the race itself was evident from her bony structure, her greying hair which still showed a streak or two of red, and the cold grey eyes with which she surveyed me.

"Macdougal, my dear, here is a treat for you! A fellow-countrywoman of yours and Sir Walter Scott's! Ah, the great Sir Scott! How I was made to read him in the original when I was learning English!"

Miss Macdougal bowed coldly. "I trust Cavtat makes you sufficient enjoyment?" she asked.

Even her English had grown rusty with the years. As if conscious of that, she lapsed into French. Her French, like that of Madame Pachitsh herself, was the French of Middle Europe, spoken heavily, with a drag. When I asked what part of Scotland she came from, she replied, "Perth. But a long while ago. I have no relatives, no friends there left." And she said it with such decision as to imply clearly, "And no interest either."

Perhaps the old lady sensed that this clan reunion was not going very well. Perhaps she merely wished to have a few words with the captain in private. At any rate, after we had finished tea she suggested that the ex-governess should show me over the house. Stiffly Miss Macdougal bowed and, as one accustomed to obeying orders, rose to her feet and motioned me out of the room.

I was neither puzzled nor hurt by her behaviour, for I had met it before and understood it. I had met such elderly governesses before. Their working days done, they existed like cabbages in corners of the castles and country-houses of Central Europe. They lived under the feudal system which decrees that, while every inch of loyalty was exacted during their working years, they must be housed and fed in old age and treated as a privileged pet of the family.

But to give all one's loyalty means to sever one's own links with its orange and cream tiles and its black marble floor : all one's country until all relatives and friends are dead or forgotten. To flinch from the very name of one's birthplace because it evokes memories long dead, as I saw Miss Macdougal flinched now. That was the price paid for comfort, protection, and, finally, the privilege of burial in a family vault in some foreign land.

Miss Macdougal led me first to inspect Madame Pachitsh's own little boudoir. Because of the steep slope of the hill, this was on the next floor, but on a level with a garden terrace above the one by the gate. Here, too, a sophisticated and exquisite taste had furnished the room. The chintzes and hangings were of blue and white *toile de jouy*; a darkish blue, almost sapphire. The mirror, the writing-desk, and the table were of white-painted Empire, much simpler than the Empire furniture down below and lacking its gilt. A huge bowl of yellow roses stood on the table. And the glazed blue-and-white curtains were looped back from a french window leading directly on to this second little garden overhanging the first.

The moment the glass door was thrust back, all the fragrance of that garden rushed in to greet us. Orange and lemon trees grew in the round centre bed. "In spring that bed is just a cushion of violets," Miss Macdougal announced behind me. "The big scented Russian ones," she added.

A small pavilion looked at me from across the flower-bed. "That is the guest-house," she proclaimed with her hoarse, foreign accent. Then she gave a small, superior smile. "Here with us we consider it more practical to house our guests under a separate roof."

Here with us. How stupid to feel sad on Miss Macdougal's behalf, when she obviously did not feel so on her own ! And yet this claim to vicarious ownership was somewhat pathetic. It underlined the fact that, now, all she probably had in the world was a boxful of clothes and the crucifix round her neck.

But I enjoyed seeing over that guest-house. I couldn't help comparing it with the whitewashed wall and the rusty iron bedstead of my own room above the restaurant on the quay. The delicate chintzes, this time English, sprigged with lily-of-the-valley, the chaise-longue placed so that the occupant could look straight out at the little garden; the bathroom next door with its orange and cream tiles and its black marble floor : all this made me for the first time definitely discontented with the room I would have to go back to.

But first we returned to the half-sunk drawing-room. Two women callers had arrived during our absence. Beautifully made up, very vivacious and hanging with pearls, they greeted me with effusion as though they had never seen me before. But we had exchanged glances, for all that, as they came out from the red-and-white villa straight opposite the little restaurant on the quay.

"How enchanting to meet an English writer in this primitive corner of the world!" they exclaimed.

Something stirred in the recesses of Miss Macdougal's mind and rose to her lips. "Scottish," she said coldly. . . .

That was the first of many afternoon visits to the old lady sitting in her cool vault with the plum-coloured curtains. To tell the truth, I was glad of an object for a stroll where, at the end of it, one could find a chair in which to sit down. Otherwise, in the whole of Cavtat I had only the one wooden chair in my room, the iron one in the restaurant on the quay, and a rush-bottomed one in church. Day after day the burning sun beat down on the Adriatic, on the brown rocks above it, on the sharp little flinty walks leading around the coast. And if one got suddenly tired, there was nowhere, not even a few feet of grass, not even a patch of sand, where one might cushion oneself.

The shingle, over which the green waters flowed and then ebbed, was composed of extremely sharp pieces of broken-off rock. The pathway bordering it was as hard as flint, though edged by grey-green bushes of rosemary which, when the sun was full out, scented the air deliciously. If one walked too far along it, one was exhausted long before one returned to the quay. And the iron chairs there were not meant to be sat on, anyway, except while one was actually eating; while from there it was still a hard climb up to one's bare little room again.

But in between, in the afternoons anyway, there was always one of Madame Pachitsh's wonderful, padded chairs to sit down on.

Cavtat was like a beautiful Greek statue, alluring but hard as stone. And its one great tourist attraction, the mausoleum, was the same. This stood, white in the bright fierce light, on its separate knoll high above the water, offering only an empty beauty (no seats) once one had climbed up to it. It had been planned and decorated with majestic carved seraphim, by Mestrovitch, Yugoslavia's famous sculptor. It was a memorial to seven members of the rich ship-owning family whose villa faced me on the quay. They had all died, one after the other, in the epidemic of Spanish influenza which had swept Europe after the close of the First World War. I would gaze up at those solemn angel faces, wishing that I too were beyond fatigue. Then leave the cold marble interior to stumble down to sea-level again, regretting that the Racic family had not thought of endowing a few seats for visitors while they were at it.

19

ONE day a new arrival was led to his place in the restaurant down by the quay.

We all studied him surreptitiously over our soup. He was young, fairish, and very gaudily dressed. His suit was obviously new, extremely padded at the shoulders, but very badly cut. His shirt was worn open at the neck as a concession to the heat and the holiday mood. The day he arrived, he was wearing bright yellow suède shoes, but later, after letting them make their effect on us, he fell back on sandshoes like everyone else.

The fat Czech girl, Linda, ogled him at first, until the sun caught the glint of gold on his wedding-ring finger, when she turned her chair sideways and sulked, disappointed, with her back to him. Apparently he was a Slovene, from some little village up in the north. For he seemed lonely, and talked a lot to old Franz, though what language they talked in I don't know, as he was too young to have remembered German, the old lingua franca of Slovenia when it was in the Empire.

It was Franz who told us why he had come here to Cavtat. "He is on his honeymoon," he said impressively; adding, "All young Brautpaar like to come south, to see the Adriatic. It is so romantische, nicht?"

"But where is his Braut?" I asked.

"Oh, there was not money enough for them both to take a holiday. Besides, it seems he owns the village shop, and she has to stay behind and look after it."

Franz seemed to think this only common sense, though it didn't appear very romantische to me. The young man, too, seemed a little bored now and then. When it was full moon, I would see him standing on the edge of the quay gazing impressively up at the moon. And I am quite sure Linda would have loved to console him, but her careful parents had already swept her indoors.

Most days, he took his breakfast fully garbed in his best, and then hastened on to the little steamer which called shortly after with the mails. It was apparently much more chic to say one had spent one's honeymoon in Dubrovnik, which everyone knew, than at a cheap little hole like Cavtat. So to Dubrovnik he went to enjoy himself. Once or twice I encountered him there, sitting in Gradska's Café, or peering at the souvenir shops, but always, immaculately, alone. This honeymoon was evidently to be shared in spirit with the loved one far off in Slovenia.

His one heavy expenditure was in postcards. He was always scribbling on them as he sipped his coffee, or if I caught a glimpse of him on the street in Dubrovnik, he would be thoughtfully going through the rack of coloured views, selecting the ones with the bluest skies and the greenest sea.

" Does he send them all to his Braut?" I asked Franz one day.

The old man nodded. "Natürlich! It must be for her as good as seeing the things by his side. He told me he has bought an album, colossally large and bound in real leather. He has even gone to heavy expense in having both his name and hers, and the date of the honeymoon, lettered on its outside in gold. The postcards will go in there. Together they mean to mount them when he gets back. It will be a souvenir for their children, nicht?"

For myself, when I went to Dubrovnik, I was fascinated by the dark outline of the Island of Lokrum, which just showed on the horizon beyond the bay. I would sit gazing at it as I sipped my own coffee at Gradska's, remembering what the Viennese woman had told me about it.

There, in the heart of the island, hidden by the trees which almost covered the island itself, lay the most forgotten of the royal palaces once belonging to the Habsburgs. It had been built in the nineteenth century, in the sugar-icing style beloved by them. There were marble terraces and pseudo-classic statuary, and everything which is sadder now and more dated than the ruins of more than a thousand years ago. The marble was green and neglected; not kept in the immaculate condition of a genuine tourist attraction. The openings between the trees, planned to give glimpses of the sea to anyone sitting on the terraces, had narrowed into mere green funnels laced with overgrown branches. . . .

"Not that I have ever seen it myself," added the Viennese, crossing herself hurriedly and adding, "God be thanked!"

"Then how do you know how it looks?" I asked.

"Because, just after the war, my cousin Hildegard went there on an excursion with her parents. She told me about it. She was only a child, but she had heard them speak of the ill-luck of each of the Habsburgs who had ever lived there. She said she could feel their unhappiness in the air. . . . Of course, Hildegard is too imaginative, even now. Still, if ever a place was cursed. . . ."

And on whom had the curse come down? First, of course, on the Empress Elizabeth herself. Perhaps not first, after all. Because, before she had died under the murderer's knife, she had given or lent the palace to her brother and sister-in-law. And he, Maximilian, called to be Emperor of Mexico, had been shot, and his wife, Carlotta, ended her days a hopeless lunatic. Not there, but in Brussels. Still, she had spent some time in Lokrum. Perhaps those two beautiful ghosts, Elizabeth and Carlotta, still swept the terraces with their crinolines after the sun had gone down.

"At any rate, I would not care to risk going there," the Viennese said with decision. Her eyes dilated as she added, "What if one got lost in the wood and missed the boat back?"

There was a small steamer which crossed to Lokrum and gave one a few hours there. I certainly meant to take it, but the time of its sailing was awkward. The morning boat from Cavtat arrived just too late to catch the other. One would really have to stay the night in Dubrovnik, and do it that way. But just now, at the height of the season, the hotels were all full and expensive. . . .

"Crown Prince Rudolph visited Lokrum too," my Viennese

friend was informing me. "And you know what happened to *him*!"

I had been told that the Crown Prince had a passion for exotic birds. He had indulged in one of his whims by letting loose on the island brilliantly coloured macaws, parakeets, green talking parrots, and the vivid small birds coloured like butterflies, sent to him from his uncle's empire in South America. It had pleased him to fancy that, even when he was not there, the avenues between the dark trees could suddenly flash with colour, and that the harsh mocking tones of the birds would echo here instead of his own, when he was far away.

But after his mysterious death, none of his family cared to visit the island any more. His mother could not bear it, and the tragedy of Maximilian and Carlotta had already taken place. So the great white villa was left abandoned, kept theoretically in order by a skeleton staff, until the fall of the Habsburg dynasty.

Now (said the Viennese) it is really an orphan home, run by some nuns. The little girls run about the terraces in long, old-fashioned pinafores, for my cousin Hildegard saw them. But she thought them unnaturally quiet, those children. There were few of them, anyway, and they did not make themselves felt nearly so much as did the shadow of the lovely Empress Elizabeth, seated on her chaise-longue at the end of the terrace, watching them play.

"What happened to the birds?" I asked. "They will have died long ago, of course. Killed by the first winter storms that beat on Lokrum. After all, the Adriatic is not a tropical climate."

"Of course." The Viennese nodded her head. "Naturally, they must have died long ago."

She had bought a large silk handkerchief of tawny orange, in one of the gift shops in Dubrovnik, I remember. It was to ring the changes on her grey flannel suit; she planned to wear it along with the lemon-coloured blouse, just showing out of her pocket in a flame-coloured slit. I had admired the idea and had watched her trying it out. Now I remember how her hands played with it on her lap; twisting it nervously round and round into bracelets for her brown wrists.

"Naturally, they must have died," she repeated. "And anything the people say here is just pure superstition. . . ."

I waited.

"And yet," she said, frowning a little, "Hildegard always swears that she saw it herself."

"Saw what? Did she see one of the birds?"

"Of course not! How could she when they could not have outlived one summer season! That's what I always tell her. Even their nests, if they made them, even their moulted feathers, could scarcely have lasted for fifty years!"

"Then what was it your cousin Hildegard saw?"

"A—a feather. A long green parrot-feather lying on one of the paths through the wood. But when she bent down to pick it up, a puff of wind lifted it right out of her hand."

"Perhaps——"

"No." She shook her head. "The orphanage didn't have any pet birds. Of course, Hildegard was only a child at the time. But a feather fifty years old. . . ."

So, each time I looked towards Lokrum I said to myself I must really go over and visit it tomorrow. The thought of an island haunted by a fall of exotic feathers charmed and did not frighten me. After all, I wouldn't be spending the night there; only a few hours. And, dark though it looked on the horizon, the sea between it and myself sparkled and danced so gaily that the sail over to the island was bound to be pleasant in itself. That stretch of water was one beloved of a school of dolphins. So I sat on in Gradska's Café, watching their fins make a golden arc. Saying to myself, tomorrow. . . .

And then I woke up with a start to find it was autumn already. The Czech family had gone home. The bridegroom had taken his departure with his pockets stuffed with postcards which he was too thrifty to mail now that he would see his bride so soon. My Viennese friend was going into Dubrovnik to see about her ticket back to Vienna, and I thought I had better go with her and take mine too.

There seemed to be no time left. I called upon old Madame Pachitsh to say good-bye. She, too, was preparing to leave for the winter. "One must return to the world some time!" she remarked with a smile.

Miss Macdougal saw me to the gate. "Have you any message for Scotland?" I asked.

Her eyes suddenly looked as if they were peering at something very far away. Then they gave up the effort and met mine instead. "No, thank you," she said.

Part Five

A FLAT IN DRESDEN

20

DURING the winter, from time to time, I remembered Lokrum. That was a lesson, I said to myself. A lesson to do everything one wants to while there is time. I did not feel myself that the time was getting short, but there must have been something in the air, some ominous stillness such as warns the traveller to get to his destination before the storm bursts.

Of course the news in the papers was alarming, but it had been alarming for years. It did not seem to have any effect on the tourist industry. People happily made their plans to go abroad in the spring, and I made mine too. The German State Railways were just as lavish as ever with their free passes for travel to journalists like myself. The Press Attaché at the Czechoslovak Legation in London obtained the same facilities for me, and gave me a letter of introduction to his opposite number in Prague. I shall go to Berlin first (I said), and then through Dresden to Prague, and beyond to the Tatra Mountains.

But there was a change in the air of the Pension Schmolke. I felt it directly I entered the place. Indeed, before, while I still stood on the threshold, waiting for one of Frau Schmolke's little maids to open the door. For, at the side of the bell-pull there was that aggressive little button testifying to the fact that the owner of this flat subscribed to the Winter Help Fund and all the necessary Party organizations.

Frau Schmolke herself opened the door. I had not had time to remove my eye from the Winterhilfe button, and she began at once, speaking defensively, without giving me her usual warm greeting.

"Ach, that! I had to give in at last. . . . They so pestered me, those officials, for ever ringing the door-bell to know why the button was not there! I believe in doing good when one can, but not advertising it on one's own door-step. Have I not kept One-Dish Sunday always, since you have known me, just the same?"

"Yes, indeed," I said, stepping into the hall.

"And today is Sunday, the first of the month!" she exclaimed triumphantly; adding, "You will see for yourself whether I help the nation or not!"

She had changed in appearance as well as in manner; to have grown thinner, less majestic even. Before, she had always proclaimed aloud the unspoken belief of half Berlin, that the money raised by One-Dish Sunday went straight into the Funds of the Party instead of into the pockets of the poor. Now, after one glance at her face, I knew better than to remind her of that.

"I have managed to reserve for you your old room," she went on more cheerfully. "The Colonel wanted it for himself when he came, but I was able to persuade him that it was noisier there, on the street."

"I thought you never——"

"Hush!" She caught my arm suddenly, glancing at the closed door we were passing. "The *pension* is no longer for artists only, that would indeed be too selfish." She raised her voice as she spoke the words. "You will find many old friends here still. But I have had—I have gladly set aside one or two rooms for those in other professions. It is as well to be brought into wider currents of life."

The room was the same, but nothing else. And even the room did not seem so highly polished, so spick and span as before. The white mat on top of my bedside table, the antimacassars over the chairs, did not gleam quite so brightly with whiteness and starch. Frau Schmolke first pushed the door to behind us before she apologized.

"You remember my three little Mädschen who helped me here with the housework? I am left only with one. Nowadays the girls seem mad to join this Service or the other, to live in camps, to wear uniform, to do anything but to enter a private

house! They are told it is more patriotic. . . . I am too old to go
down on my knees and polish floors, and the girl I have now
has no time. Believe me, Fräulein, I am tired. But so tired!"

That was it. Those lines on her face were not, after all, ones
of anxiety or fear. They must be lines of fatigue. And if she
were not so immaculately dressed as usual, if she had even forgotten to put on her ear-rings, surely that could be put down to
exhaustion and not to anything else?

"It is the same at home," I assured her. "All the girls want to
work in factories. They don't go into domestic service any
more."

There was a small sound behind us. She looked round
quickly. Her nerves must be in very bad order, for she had suddenly gone quite pale. The door had not been properly latched.
Now it was being pressed open by the body of a small dachs-
hund which had thrust its nose in like a knife and was peering
at us, bright-eyed.

"Ach, it is only Hansi!" she cried, relieved.

"I thought you didn't allow dogs."

"But this is the Colonel's dog. Go, Hansi! Canst thou not
open thy master's door? Then I will open it for thee."

And she had gone quickly out of the room.

I unpacked thoughtfully. Soon the great brass bell, whose
note I remembered so well, began to echo along the corridors,
summoning everyone to the midday meal. As Frau Schmolke
had said, this was One-Dish Sunday. It had been inaugurated
some years earlier, ostensibly to raise funds for the poor during
Berlin's bitter winter weather. On that day every housewife was
begged, as a patriotic duty, to serve only one dish at the midday
meal. The sums thus saved by not indulging in extra fuel, in
pastries or fruit to finish the meal, were set aside to be collected
by officials who came round each district on Monday morning.
Frau Schmolke had always said loudly and firmly that while she
approved of the aim, she distrusted its carrying out. Never (it
appeared) were any balance-sheets published. And who paid
the wages of the men who came round from door to door?

No. She would dispense her own charity to the poor. What she saved once a month by not giving us our usual lavish Sunday repast she gave, as I knew, to an old woman, an ex-servant from her more prosperous past, who lived from hand to mouth in a slum in the heart of Berlin. She always explained to newcomers what she was doing, and congratulated us upon our charitable impulses. It had been one of her little jokes. But the button fixed to the door-bell showed that she did not make that joke any more.

It was always, nevertheless, a good, hearty meal. I think the single dish served approached more to Lancashire hotpot than anything else. Good beef stewed a long time with every sort of vegetable, and perhaps a handful of rice or barley, in a large iron pot, is by no means to be despised. She served it in deep plates, with forks and spoons, and thick slices of bread to put in the gravy, and a small cup of fragrant black coffee afterwards. I could smell the stew already as I walked down the passage towards the dining-room at the end.

I could also hear a loud voice, talking steadily, obviously monopolizing the conversation in a way that Frau Schmolke had never permitted before. I opened the door. There sat Gertrud Orff, Nicolai, the little bald chorus-master from the opera, two meek Germans from the provinces, the Polish woman pianist, and a tall, square man in a Colonel's uniform.

He went right on talking as though I had not come into the room. And the others, even Frau Schmolke herself, sat listening respectfully with their eyes on his face; all except Nicolai, who kept his on his plate and spooned away silently, and the Pole, who gave me a half-bow and smile of recognition.

The Colonel saw her greeting and stopped, annoyed. The Pole helped herself to some bread and asked serenely and pleasantly, in French, what I had been doing with myself since she saw me last? I was surprised at her friendliness, since she had always kept herself aloof from everyone. But I realized that it had been assumed in order to bring a temporary halt to the lecture, as well as to rebuke those who had not the courage to greet me themselves.

The Colonel recovered his position as well as he could. "So we have an English guest? Come, sit by me here, Fräulein. Do not be afraid of the savage German soldier. You are all afraid of us, nicht? Your newspapers say we eat babies and tear them apart with our hands!"

"Do they?" I said, seating myself at the empty place he indicated.

He had spoken banteringly, evidently trying to be agreeable. But now his expression darkened. "Your newspapers tell lies! Lies!" He banged his fist on the table. "How can the two greatest nations in Europe get along if one tells lies about the other?"

There was a rigid attitude right round the table. I picked up my spoon and took a mouthful of stew. He looked down sideways at me for a moment. Then he glanced across at the Polish woman, and his face darkened again.

"You have signed a pact with Poland. Against whom? Who do you suppose is going to attack her? Is it sane to wish to ally oneself with a race of decadent aristocrats who rely on outmoded cavalry which one good machine-gun, one line of tanks, could blow into——"

The Polish woman rose with great dignity and left the room.

There followed an uncomfortable silence. Only Nicolai had enough aplomb to break it. "So you've started again on your travels?" he said pleasantly. "And where do they lead you this year?"

"First to Dresden," I told him, "and then Prague. But I won't be very long in Prague, because I want to get on to the Tatra Mountains."

"So. Dresden." The Colonel spoke before Nicolai could reply. "The City of Baroque. The City of Augustus the Strong. Music too. There all the arts meet on the bank of the Elbe." And he proceeded to give us a dissertation upon German Baroque. He knew what he spoke about. He was clear, simple, and informative. I listened with interest, because, after all, I wanted to learn.

But then he began on the Czechs. Had I heard what the

Czechs were doing now, this very moment, to the wretched German population of the Sudetenland? No, of course not, because my English newspapers would not have told me. But he would. Now.

It was a painful story, and it went on and on. I had visited Czechoslovakia before; I had even lived in the house of a Sudeten German woman and had heard most of his arguments already. I also knew those for the other side; the side of a people who had been under the Austrian yoke for centuries, and who were, all things considered, remarkably tolerant and fair, so far as government of their new minority was concerned, although individually they sometimes failed to resist the temptation to get some of their own back.

So I did not have to attend very closely to what the Colonel was saying. I could watch the faces round the table instead. And there I read, for the first time, hearty agreement with him. Their expressions were not put on to please the man who, I saw, now ruled the Pension Schmolke. They were indignant and sincere. Only Nicolai's expression I could not read, for he kept his head down obstinately over his plate.

Perhaps the Colonel noticed this too. For presently he left Czechoslovakia and began to speak about Russia instead. "You British are wooing the Russian Bear," he told me angrily, "you don't know what you are doing! Can East and West think alike? Listen, I make a prophecy!" He pushed his chair sideways from the table so as to lift a finger right in my face. "The time will come when England and Germany will have to fight the Russian Bear side by side! Yes, we may fight one another first. We may fight others first. But in the end you will turn to us, as the only bulwark left. Ask the Polish lady who was so indignant at my remarks about her country's antediluvian army! Ask—yes, ask Herr Nicolai here!"

Nicolai raised his head slowly. "I'm prepared to fight alongside any army that gains me the right to an honest passport and not just a piece of white paper," he said.

Gertrud Orff had sat silent through all this. She had not even given me a friendly glance since I entered the room. Had she changed too? But as we rose from table and left it together, I felt her arm slipped into mine. "Come into my room while I make some more coffee," she whispered; adding, "We can talk more comfortably there."

The rooms in the Pension Schmolke varied in price. When Gertrud first arrived from Hamburg, she had taken one of the larger, more expensive ones. After a little, finding she made no headway in gaining pupils, she had had to leave it for a much smaller one overlooking the courtyard at the back. Apparently, during my absence she had gained some success. For the room into which she now ushered me was one of the best in the house.

She plugged in her electric coffee machine. "You mustn't mind that old fool of a Colonel," she said with her back to me, "his bluster is all on the surface. Really, in some ways he can be quite soft-hearted. You should see the fuss he makes over his little dog Hansi!"

I looked around the room. She had introduced all sorts of comforts to make it an agreeable home. When she came first, she had often bewailed the selling of her own piano before she left Hamburg, and had complained of the worn condition of the practice-pianos Frau Schmolke had installed in two of the rooms. To buy one then had been out of the question. Now I saw an upright Bechstein against the wall.

"You are looking at my new piano? I got it at a bargain, I assure you! Second-hand, but no more than five years old, and carefully used too. What is more, it came from a Christian household; I made it my business to find that out."

I did not understand what she meant. Seeing this, she dropped her voice. "They have been selling off the stuff from Jewish households cheaply. It would stick in my throat to get that sort of a bargain."

The coffee bubbled. She detached the glass globe from its metal holder and poured out two cups. "I have to be back at my work at three. But you are welcome to stay on and try my piano if you like——"

"Don't you have your pupils in here then?" I asked.

"My—pupils? But I have none!"

I was puzzled. I knew she had to work for her living and that she had found work of some sort, and well-paid work too, seemed obvious. She looked puzzled too, then laughed suddenly and leaned forward, patting my knee.

"But I never told you! When you last saw me, I was in despair at finding no pupils, nicht?"

"Yes. You said something about nobody daring to take lessons from you because you didn't belong to the Party——"

She interrupted me hurriedly. "I forgot there were other ways of killing the cat than by wringing its neck! After all, a musician of wide experience like myself must be of some use, even if her own voice is failing! So now I test other peoples' voices for our radio station here."

"Oh, Gertrud, I'm glad! It sounds a splendid job. And if you're able to take this room and buy that piano, it must be a well-paid one too."

She nodded rather complacently. "The salary is quite generous. It was young Holz, the chorus-master, who put me up to applying for the job. Naturally, with his connexions he knows of all the plums going."

I glanced at her little gold travelling clock ticking away over the stove. There were still twenty minutes, and she didn't seem ready to hurry me away.   "Tell me what it is you do, exactly," I said.

She finished her coffee and set down the cup. "Well, as you know, every young singer is anxious to get on the radio, it is such good advertisement for them. Requests for auditions pour in in hundreds. They have to be weeded out——"

"Why, Gertrud!" I looked at her with awe. "You don't mean to say you have to spend all day and every day listening to hundreds and hundreds of people who think they can sing!" I thought now that, no matter how high her salary was, she certainly earned it.

She burst out laughing. "Not all of them, stupid! Only those who have passed the panel already." And then, curiously, she stopped dead. It seemed a harmless enough remark to have made, but one would have thought she had covered her mouth.

"Oh," I said, relieved. "You mean there's a panel that weeds out the voices first?"

There was no doubt of it. All her elation had suddenly left her. "Not the voices. The applicants have—have to convince the panel that they are sincere members of the Party. Then they are handed on to me."

There was a moment's silence.

At last I said, "Do you seriously believe that only members of the National Socialist Party can sing?"

She got very red. "Of course not. But the radio is a powerful weapon. One must preserve its purity. One must make sure that nothing comes over the air to undermine the State."

"Do you think the songs of Brahms or Hugo Wolf would undermine the State?"

"You don't understand!" she said angrily. "And I have no time to explain, because I must now dress and go out to my afternoon auditions."

She sprang to her feet and began rummaging in the huge black armoire which served as a wardrobe. It was still spring and the weather unusually cold. If she had brought out a new fur coat, I think I would have been angrier still. I was relieved, and in some curious way mollified, to see her thrust herself into a light blue coat in which I had seen her before. She went quickly over to her mirror, jammed on a felt hat and picked up her bag and gloves. Rushed though her movements were, however, she seemed reluctant to turn round and face me on her way to the door.

"Does this mean that you have joined the Party yourself?" I asked.

She turned round at last. Her face was still flushed, and there were tears in her eyes.

"Do you think I wanted to? Everything I said to you last year I mean still in my heart. An artist has to have integrity, yes? An artist must keep clear of politics; must judge of art on its own merits and not because it is stamped as approved by the State. . . . Yes, but an artist must live first, in order even to think these things. Do you think it would have done any good if I'd starved?"

"I never realized before that Herr Holz must have been a member of the Party too," I said slowly, "I mean, all along."

"Of course!" She sounded contemptuous. "How else did he land a State appointment? After I had been here long enough to learn how things were in Berlin I used to tremble, yes tremble, at the things Frau Schmolke would say before him. Luckily she has learned to hold her tongue, and so have I."

She moved towards the door, then hesitated. "All the same, you are welcome to use my piano," she said.

"Thanks," I said, "but I don't feel musical."

21

ALTHOUGH it was May, a cold little wind kept blowing down the Kurfürstendamm so that the café tables were empty along the pavements and everyone sat indoors. The passers-by hurried along, wearing their overcoats still. The luxury goods, the fine leather handbags, the rhinestone necklaces and elegant powder compacts, shone in their glass cases along the kerb, but there were no flowers at their base as yet, and one could imagine that the tender leaves coming out in the Tiergarten were being thoroughly nipped.

I was taking my lunch in an automat. The Colonel was always back at the Pension Schmolke for lunch, mainly, I suspected, to make sure that Hansi got his. I did not want another encounter with him. He was generally out for dinner, and Hansi, like most well-brought-up children, was given a last meal much earlier, so did not have to be considered.

The automatic machines showed their contents through glass. A well-muffled old gentleman stood beside me, his ten-pfennig coins in his hand, unable to make up his mind. I made up mine. First a coin through the slit which showed tempting dark brown and orange slices of rye bread and cheese. The sandwich slid out to me on a tray. Then an apple. And, finally, up to the counter for a glass of milk.

I took my lunch to a table beside the window. No doubt it was only the weather, but I felt very depressed. I looked at the people hurrying by, and thought they all looked depressed too, and anxious as well. Suddenly I was conscious of a pair of pale blue, fishlike eyes staring at me from under a shabby hat brim.

It was Mr Smith. I had almost forgotten the odd and furtive Englishman whom the Frauenwerke people had been so anxious for me to meet. I remembered his agitated championship of his adopted country, and wondered again what anyone had thought would be gained by subjecting me to it. Perhaps if we spoke to each other again, I might find out. . . .

So I waved. But immediately the eyes slid away from me and, though he had momentarily halted, he scurried off, not even lifting his hat. More. I saw him give a furtive glance round, as if to assure himself that none of the passers-by had noticed my greeting. For a moment I watched him dart through the crowd like a frightened fish, and then he was lost.

"What are you staring at?" Nicolai's voice sounded behind me. We both used this café quite often, and had, in fact, arranged to meet here; but he had said that he might be late and I was to start without him. He had made his selection from the automat already, and sat down with the plateful of sandwiches before him. I told him about Mr Smith.

He seemed to understand the enigma at once. "A renegade," he said, nodding his head over his mouthful of sandwich. "There are some in every country you know, even in England. First, he was used to sound you as to your usefulness, journalistically speaking. But you weren't really of much use, were you? So he is taking no chances of seeming to have kept up the acquaintanceship."

I did not reply. Berlin seemed colder and more depressing than ever. Was it possible that I had once been so happy here? He sensed my unhappiness at once.

"By Bolshevik standards I am a renegade too," he said soothingly, "though I have at least never tried to conceal the fact. I just can't accept the present régime there. That's all."

"Where are your friends?" I asked, for he had specially required me to be at the café that morning in order to introduce them to me.

"Oh, they will be here directly!" He became animated at once. "It was sheer providence that I met them, separately, on different occasions. Don't you believe in providence? They are both Australians. They will advise me about my tour."

Poor Nicolai! So he was still planning his concert tour in Australia. I hoped for his sake that his new friends were rich. Very rich and influential. For I had not lived among musicians without knowing that, for an unknown singer to embark on a tour, it was absolutely necessary to have big financial backing, or to have attracted the attention of an impresario brave enough to take risks.

The woman arrived first. She was plainly dressed, quiet, and middle-aged. She turned out to be the wife of a doctor in Melbourne and was making her first trip to Europe. She had gone up shyly to Nicolai at the close of a light concert in an hotel at which he had been singing, and had congratulated him. Enchanted to find that she came from Australia, he had immediately, and with his usual unself-consciousness, invited her to have a sandwich with him next day, at this inexpensive automat, and to tell him about her native land.

"I asked you, too, because she might feel easier with another woman present," he murmured, as she made her way towards us, threading between the little tables.

The second arrival looked decidedly more prosperous and therefore a better bet. He was a rich sheep-farmer who had invited Nicolai to have a drink with him after the concert. Large, kindly, and elderly, he made a pleasant guest. But it was immediately clear that his knowledge of, and his interest in, music were nil.

Still Nicolai persevered. I could not but wonder that he had not realized, long before the drink at the hotel bar was finished, what completely useless material he was cultivating. Apparently, however, he hadn't. They had talked about Melba, it seemed. The sheep-farmer had known her family, and his natural pride in this link with the Australian Nightingale had blinded Nicolai to his complete disinterest in the songs she sang.

The sheep-farmer, in his turn, had obviously been drawn to Nicolai, not by his singing but by the fact that he was a real live Russian. He plied Nicolai with questions about Russia, and was dissatisfied and disappointed at the brief answers he got.

"I was only a lad at the time of the Revolution," Nicolai explained, giving his charming, apologetic smile, "and, to tell you the truth, I have been trying to forget it ever since."

Then he plunged back eagerly into the search for information about the musical life of Australia. Would it not be possible to organize a little tour right into the interior, from one sheep-station, say, to the next? Were there not perhaps school-houses, halls, within reasonable distance of one or two farms, where people could gather and forget their hard work in an hour or two of music?

The sheep-farmer answered Nicolai as though his questions had been made in Russian. Quite obviously he did not understand them at all. But he was firm about sheep-farms not specially requiring music. Then he turned the conversation to racing, and the doctor's wife joined in eagerly. For such a quiet, meek little woman it was amazing how much she knew. And now it was the turn of Nicolai and myself to sit listening, all at sea and restless for the conversation to become general again.

The Australians took their departure. They seemed glad to have met one another, for both were apparently lonely amid the intricacies of an older civilization. They made arrangements to meet each other again, and pressed Nicolai warmly to dine with them at their hotels. I thought he would be too disappointed to accept. But I heard him do so with alacrity and pleasure.

After they had walked out of the café together, I turned to console him. To my astonishment he did not seem to need it. "They were nice people, don't you think?" he said eagerly. "They would help me if I ever went to Australia, you heard them say so, didn't you?"

His eyes were shining. He looked like a happy child. I could not bear to dash the light out of them, though I knew that the invitations he had heard were only the warm-hearted offers of private hospitality which Australians give without stint.

"Look here, Elisabeth," he said, pulling two tickets out of his pocket, "Holz has given me these for tonight. For Lorzing's *Undine*. The Goebbels Ministerium has spread itself over the mounting, so I'm afraid it will be very Kitsch. But will you go with me? I feel that I want to celebrate."

To celebrate what? I was conscious of the two different traits which could exist side by side in the Russian, and especially in

Nicolai. There was the strain of psychological insight, which had led him, even without seeing Mr Smith, to read that riddle at once, and to place everyone exactly before they had been five minutes at the Pension Schmolke.

And there was the strain of self-delusion which could persuade him that the impossible was not even difficult. Perhaps that strain had been of necessity over-cultivated in the emigrant, for it was only Russian emigrants whom I knew. Perhaps it had not existed so strongly when they still had a home and background and therefore no necessity to cultivate it as an opiate to mask reality.

Anyway, I said I would go to *Undine*.

That night I was astonished to meet Frau Schmolke rustling in her long skirts along the passage towards the dining-room. It was Monday night, when she invariably went to a small bridge club which met in the house of a friend of hers. We were first in the dining-room and alone. I said, "But your bridge club, Gnädige Frau? It meets no longer?"

"No longer." She cast an apprehensive glance towards the door. "We thought it inexpedient to meet so regularly, even though our object was merely a friendly game. Nowadays, here in Berlin, even regular meetings among friends have become— inadvisable."

Someone was coming along the passage. She stopped with a look of apprehension which stabbed me. But it was only Herr Holz. Only? I saw for the first time that he looked smug. Why had I not noticed that quiet smugness before?

"So you and Nicolai are going to patronize *Undine* tonight?" he said, unfolding his napkin and tying it round his neck. "Tonight I do not conduct. It is my free evening. But I looked in at the rehearsals, and it goes well. Lorzing's music is a bit faded and old-fashioned perhaps. But the thing has charm."

One by one the others arrived, all but the Pole, whom I had not seen at table since the Colonel had chosen to insult the military might of her country. Since then she had asked to have her meals given to her in her own room on a tray, until he chose to depart. Nicolai was wearing his best suit and an air of feverish excitement. I saw he was still living in his dream. And the dream of *Undine* was to be a celebration of that.

Goebbels' Ministry of Culture must have given a big grant to the production. In the eyes of solid musicians it might be Kitsch, but the lavishness of the scenes brought back the exquisite illustrations to a *de luxe* copy of the old fairy-tale which I had had once as a child. The fisherman's cottage was simple enough. When the fisherman brought in his find, the girl with the lovely, soulless eyes, the fairy-tale had begun. It was during the forest scene, when she spoke with her uncle, that the machinery of pantomime got its chance. And yet I gasped with the rest of the audience when, interrupted in his conversation with his water-nymph niece, the uncle stepped back towards the forest stream, and immediately a great gush of water rose, wavering, like a fountain, to mask him from human eyes.

And there was the ballroom scene in the castle of her false Knight who, having railed at her within hearing of water, had lost her for ever. The dancers moved in a stately dream from some medieval tapestry. High on the dais sat the Knight with his new Lady. One held one's breath at her request for water from the spring in the castle yard. Had not Undine vanished into that spring, and had not her lover commanded a great stone to be placed over its mouth so that she might never return to trouble him again?

But the Lady insisted. The Page left the ballroom and returned bearing high the fatal goblet filled with spring water. One waited for what would inevitably happen now that the spring was unsealed; waited knowing who presently would enter the room. And sure enough, the lights in the torches around the wall began to flicker, to pale. The dancers stopped, as a pale blue dusk seemed to fill the room. Then the door opened slowly, slowly. And Undine drifted in, a veiled figure, to claim her lover from the side of his new bride. . . .

Kitsch, perhaps, but a spell-binding story just the same. No doubt the story was more important than the music, which made no mark then, and which I have now forgotten. But I have not forgotten Nicolai's air of still being in a dream when the curtain came down. It was no longer the opera dream, how-ever; it was his own private one of Australia, which had de-scended on him again.

We were sitting at the marble-topped table of one of the restaurants on the Unter den Linden. "I, too, have sung in opera," he said dreamily. "No doubt in Australia, too, there is sure to be an opening for a bass."

Perhaps I should not have awakened him from his dream, but it had to come some time. "Nicolai," I said, "you know as well as I do that there is no permanent opera in Australia. You know that nice sheep-farmer has no interest in music at all. And what can the wife of a Melbourne surgeon do to finance a concert tour?"

He sat staring at his plate. "Yes, I know," he said at last, in a dull, flat voice. "I was only pretending to myself." He turned on me suddenly, angry, almost savage. "Why did you spoil my pretence?"

I had done it for his own sake. Because I did not know how far his self-deception had taken him. Now I was sorry. And yet —"Tell me one thing," I begged. "Just why are you set on going to sing in Australia?"

"Because it is farthest away from Europe. America, of course. . . . But America has money enough to attract the best. My voice is no better than that of every second man in our village at home. It would be nothing exceptional, except per-haps in Australia."

"Then why don't you just go there and take your chance?"

His anger had died down. He answered me as one would answer a child. "Have you ever tried taking your chance on a Nansen Passport?"

The next day I left Berlin for Dresden.

22

THE Schmidts' flat in Dresden was an old-fashioned, spacious one in the centre of the city. Past its windows rattled the trams, going down to the royal palace and the River Elbe. Herr Schmidt, a tall, silent man whom I saw seldom, had owned a chocolate factory and had known considerable prosperity. But something happened, financially speaking, which had driven him out of business and forced his wife to take from time to time a paying guest.

I was the paying guest. I had a large room, much more pleasantly and artistically furnished than at the Pension Schmolke, for Herr Schmidt was a man of taste, and his wife was English, or so I had been told. Actually she was a Boer from South Africa, and she could not forget the Boer War. I had not been under their roof for long before I discovered that this fact had, by some curious alchemy, turned her into a perfervid Nazi.

What Herr Schmidt was I never knew. He concealed his thoughts with the utmost courtesy. But then I had discovered long ago that one could indulge in agreeable conversation with the male German much more safely than with the female—if she happened to belong to the National Socialist Party. The females were fanatics. And if, like Frau Schmidt, they had once owned British citizenship, they were apt to talk with a freedom, as between one Britisher and another, which could be painful and embarrassing at times.

Otherwise, Frau Schmidt was an agreeable and striking woman, and that in spite of being far from handsome. She was tall and well made, and had a brownish face like a horse. When dressed for the afternoon, she wore two gold Dutch coins in her ears. She had social ambitions and cultivated a wide acquaintanceship among the lesser Saxon nobility. Before I had been there long, she gave a coffee party to introduce me to some of them.

Her drawing-room was really charming. Curtains of faded brocade lined the tall windows, which rattled slightly each time a tram thundered past. An exquisite pair of Dresden candlesticks about four feet high stood in the middle of a table laden with sandwiches and cakes from Rumpelmeyer's in the Schloss Strasse. Although it was broad daylight the candles were lit, making yellow pin-points which warred with the sunshine.

I sat on her sofa conversing in English with an extremely angular lady dressed in ruby coloured velvet. A string of yellow pearls dripped down the front of it, and the feather in her hat drooped down the back. She told me she had been a former Hof-Dame at the Saxon Court.

"We miss our royal family dreadfully," she informed me. "Indeed the whole of Saxony does. Frankly, I am old-fashioned. I like to be given a lead."

I glanced quickly across at Frau Schmidt, expecting her to say that now they had the Führer to give them a lead. To my surprise, she contented herself with beginning to cut a rich chocolate cake. I was to learn that my hostess was engaged, politically speaking, in a very delicate tight-rope performance. Her sympathies were with the Nazis, but she was too bent upon retaining her friendship with members of the old régime to antagonize them unless it was really necessary.

"So do our people, they too regret the old days. The more sensible of them, anyway." An old and very corpulent General spoke up from the far corner of the room. Although he held no truck with the Nazis, his voice and manner reminded me suddenly of the Colonel's at the Pension Schmolke.

"Move over, Hermine, and let me have a word with the English Miss." The lady in red velvet moved over obediently, and there we sat, the three of us, squeezed together on Frau Schmidt's brocade-covered sofa.

"Have you heard the story of our late King's departure from Dresden?" He had a watery eye. Never before had I seen wateriness and fierceness combined. I gazed back, fascinated. "No? Then I will tell you. When, at the end of the war, the canaille decided that he must go, he went. He went in one of our local trains which had been a little disorganized by the war. That is to say, it made unscheduled halts while the line was being cleared, or the engine tied up with string, or whatever. Well——" He cleared his throat, momentarily distracted by the chocolate cake which Frau Schmidt was holding before his nose.

"Do hurry up with your story, General!" the Hof-Dame put in maliciously. It was evident that she did not like her velvets being crushed.

"I'm telling it, am I not?" His mouth was now full of cake, but he continued through it. "Well. His Majesty was bored with sitting behind drawn blinds, for some fool had told him he'd better remain invisible. So he pulled them up. There, at every halt, were lines of peasants standing respectfully, cap in hand. At every halt, as soon as they saw him they burst out cheering. And do you know what he said?"

"No," I said, since he was waiting for it.

"I was with him at the time, you know. I can vouch for it myself. When he saw them there, he flung down the window, put his head out and bawled, 'You're fine Republicans, you!' Eh, that's what he said!"

The General began to laugh. I thought he would choke, and looked on, alarmed. "Take my handkerchief," said the Hof-Dame; and then, turning to me: "He said it in our Saxon dialect, you know. It is really far funnier in the dialect."

"Yes, he always spoke it, God bless him. Talked to his people just as if he were one of themselves. Why, I remember at a palace banquet given for the Kaiser before the war, he kept chatting away in his usual form to the footman behind his chair. The Kaiser was angry, I can tell you! You should have seen how he glared. But that was just because he couldn't understand a word."

"We never cared for the Prussians," said the Hof-Dame, turning to me.

"By the Lord, no!" shouted the General, brushing cake crumbs off himself. "And now, it's worse than ever, and serve our people right! New crazy orders from Berlin every day——"

Frau Schmidt was still hovering. The lady in red velvet turned to her quickly. "How is your charming daughter Elaine?"

"Oh, she's working too hard. But next week is her name day, so she is giving a little fête. It will be a relaxation for her."

The Schmidts had a pale blonde girl who reminded me a little of Undine. She worked long hours as a secretary in the local office of the Party, but lacked her mother's enthusiasm, I could see. Through her, I was given another example of how Frau Schmidt's perfervid loyalty to the Party could be modified by personal considerations. It was shortly after the coffee party. Elaine had come down red-eyed to breakfast, confessing to have slept little. Later, when I was out of the room, she had confided the reason to her mother. Later still, her mother had told me all about it.

"Some of those small Party officials are brutes!" She added quickly, "But they would be brutes, anyway. Take a jumped-up beggar from the street, put him in uniform and give him a little authority, and you know what happens! Elaine has been gently brought up. She has met with nothing but courtesy all her life. She works hard and wishes to please. But she is new to the job, and everyone makes mistakes, don't they?"

"Well, of course."

"So instead of telling her quietly about her little mistake (a trifle it was), they shout and swear at her as if she were a cow! She did not wish to tell us of it, but you saw how silent she was at supper last night! All night she has not slept, for fear of meeting that brute today. It is cruel and stupid to break the nerve of an eager young girl!"

I agreed, but said I supposed there was nothing to be done about it. She could not leave, for instance?

Frau Schmidt shook her head. It was obviously impossible to leave. Then I saw her face harden; for the first time a British look came into it. "But I shall write to our local Gauleiter. I shall describe the whole matter, giving the name of the official in question and also Elaine's crime, which was the wrong addressing of an envelope. An envelope! I shall demand an apology...."

For the next two days there was an atmosphere of tension in the house. I believe Herr Schmidt even tried to reason his wife out of sending that letter, and Elaine crept about looking obviously terrified. But Frau Schmidt was adamant. No one would ever swear at her daughter again....

And no one did. For by return came a charming and handsome apology from the Gauleiter himself, promising that the offender would be reprimanded, and that such a thing would never happen again. Frau Schmidt waved the letter before me in triumph. "There, you see? The English think we allow ourselves to be browbeaten, and that the National Socialist Party does not know what politeness means! It takes just a little firmness——"

"From an Englishwoman," I could not help putting in.

She drew herself up, then went off at a tangent. "A Boer, if you please. I can never forget how the English behaved to our people during *that* war! Already your newspapers talk of concentration camps here in Germany. Who invented them, pray? They were first used by the English during the Boer War!"

I called after her that they were intended to protect the Boer civilians, to give them shelter and food when the tide of battle rolled over their territory, and that they were perfectly free to leave the camps as soon as their farms were once more out of the firing-line. But she had left the room.

Elaine's name-day arrived. It occasioned more excitement than usual because Frau Schmidt's social sense was to be gratified by a visit to her daughter from Princess Philippa of Hesse. The two girls were friendly, having played together since childhood. And a message had come, saying that the young Princess wished to bring her present to Elaine in person.

Frau Schmidt told me this the day before. She told me the royal call was to be made about half-past five in the afternoon. We were sitting round the table at lunch, and I thought she was making rather heavy weather of the announcement, until I realized that she was working up to a point that she wished to make, both to Elaine and me.

"Elaine, was it not for four o'clock that we settled to ask your other young friends?"

"Yes, Mama."

Her mother's brow wrinkled in calculation. Then she spoke again. "From four until half-past five is not very long. We could not be certain of having the house empty by the time the Princess arrives. Go to the telephone, dear, and ring up your friends. Tell them frankly that Princess Philippa is expected, and so you must beg them to come earlier."

Elaine's gentle looks gave way to a sullen one. "Why?"

"If they come at three, they will be ready to go by five. You must make it clear that we expect them to do so."

As Elaine still looked sullen, her mother spoke again, glancing sideways at me, so that I knew that her words were for my benefit too. "You know perfectly well that I promised Philippa's mother she would meet no one in this house with whom she was not already acquainted. On that understanding only, she is allowed to come here——"

"It is ridiculous!" Elaine burst out. "Philippa is just the same as anyone else! You are being absurdly old-fashioned. Aren't my other friends just as good as she is, now that this is a Republic?"

Frau Schmidt drew herself up. The gold coins in her ears swayed with anger. "Go to the telephone now, Elaine. Tell them the party is from three till five. I command you!"

Elaine went very slowly out of the room. Her mother looked apologetically across the table at me. "I know that such things as court etiquette have no place in the new Germany," she said (and was there a faint flavour of regret in the statement?), "but all the same, a promise is a promise. I gave mine to the Herzogin von Hesse that no one who had not been properly presented should meet her daughter under my roof. Was I not right?"

I said she was; and after a moment's pause said I thought I would make an excursion into the country, and might not come back until very late. From the relief in her face, I saw that I had said the right thing. And for the moment I was sorry for her; sorry for anyone who wished to belong to the new Germany and the old at one and the same time.

Although I had been but a short while in Dresden, I had already come across one or two women acting as nursemaids who wore a curiously medieval costume with a stiff winged cap. I was told that it was the national costume of the Wends, a very old Slav tribe, the remnants of which occupied a village a little way off. They looked like Sisters of Charity, strolling along with their little charges holding on to their skirts. Apparently they made good and reliable nursemaids, and those who could afford such luxuries still employed them.

I went out to their shuttered village, where the houses with high peaked roofs stood primly, shoulder to shoulder. I would have liked to ask questions, but there was no one to ask. Perhaps they would not have understood me if I had, for they spoke some sort of dialect of their own. But the village was empty, anyway. Everyone was in Dresden, making money some way or another.

I took a little bumbling bus through the fields, and noticed how solid and taciturn was the Saxon peasant. I could not understand what they said, either, though apparently their late King would have had no such difficulty. Now and then the bus driver took pity on me and made a remark or two about the surrounding landscape in the kind of German I could understand.

The landscape was rich and rolling. In between fields of pasturage I saw patches showing a feathery green, each before a wayside house or barnlike structure. Those were asparagus fields, he told me. But I knew the asparagus would not be the delicate, weakly kind we eat as a luxury, but the white sturdy stalks of the coarser variety which every household in Germany can afford to eat several times a week.

"Those are the places one goes to for an asparagus supper," the driver said, smacking his lips. When the season was on, whole family parties would drive out from Dresden to partake of boiled ham, asparagus, and beer. It cost very little, he informed me. A plate of buttered asparagus so high—he took one hand off the wheel to indicate its height—would cost no more than a mark.

The sun was setting and the larks had winged their way downwards to silence when I came back to the city again. The evening lights were springing up on either side of the great river. The tram which passed the gates of the royal palace rattled me up the hill and put me down at the door of the Schmidts' flat.

As I let myself into the hall with my key, I noticed a deathly silence. The party would have come to an end some time ago, and the Princess must have left too. Still, I was surprised at the hush. But perhaps the family had decided to wind up Elaine's name-day in proper fashion by taking her out to supper.

A door opened suddenly and Frau Schmidt beckoned to me. She drew me into her room and shut it carefully again. She looked as if she had been crying. "You can't imagine what a frightful afternoon I have had! Thank heaven it's over. But Elaine has gone to bed after crying her eyes out and being exceedingly rude to me. You were well out of it, I can tell you!"

It had started off all right. The girls had all come at three o'clock instead of four, as instructed. But they had not gone at five. Frau Schmidt should not have mentioned the Princess's call, for they deliberately stayed on in the hopes of seeing her.

"Those Saxon lumps!" She was so angry, she did not seek to hide her contempt for their gaucheness. "But democracy nowadays simply means that one cannot take a hint. I had left Elaine to entertain her friends herself. Sitting here, in my own room, I kept an eye on the clock. Five. Ten past five. A quarter—twenty minutes past. And the royal car due any minute! I couldn't stand it any longer. I entered the drawing-room, stood in the doorway, and said, 'Elaine and I thank you all for so graciously attending her fête. But now I must ask you to go.'"

"And did they?" I was really curious to know whether at least they would obey a command.

"They had to," she said grimly. "I circled the room till I got behind them, and then I shooed them out like the cattle they were. Have you ever heard the expression 'Saxon Coffee-cow'? That's what the rest of Germany calls our women here. Really, unless they are well-bred they are quite impossible!"

And just in time, as it seemed. For the Princess's car drove up a few moments later. Her mother's lady-in-waiting accompanied her, and actually went first into the house to make sure that no strangers polluted it, before she allowed her charge to go in.

"Fancy if she had come a few minutes earlier! Elaine gave Philippa some coffee and cakes, and managed to hold on to herself till Philippa left. Then there was an explosion! She told me I had insulted her other guests; that in the new Reich one was as good as another. That she would never overcome the shame of it, never so long as she lived. Then she ran away and locked herself into her room, and I have not seen her since."

For all her absurdity, Frau Schmidt was again an object of pity. She had kept her promise as she was bound to do; and had reaped her daughter's wrath and—who knows?—a black mark in her local Party organization. All I could do was to offer to help to clear up.

We scraped broken sandwiches off the fine Dresden plates; slid knives under rich cakes to detach them from their ornate silver cake-baskets; and I blew out the candles guttering in the delicate porcelain candlesticks because the burning wax made an unpleasant smell in the room.

23

WHEN I think of Dresden I think of a people violently divorced
from their architectural surroundings. The drab and purposeful
citizens had nothing to do with the city of Augustus the Strong.
They should have inhabited concrete boxes and travelled along
streets numbered in the American fashion. They were proud of
their baroque inheritance, but singularly lacked its graces. The
only people I had met who seemed to belong to Dresden, archi-
tecturally speaking, were the old General, and the Hof-Dame
in her red velvet and yellowing pearls.

I had forgotten Herr Geheimrat Böttger. His wife was half
Scotch and had been brought up in Glasgow. Her grandfather,
a worthy German of the old liberal principles, had acted as
tutor to King Edward VII. And she herself was as ardent a
Party member as was her friend Frau Schmidt. Indeed, she was
a fanatic on the subject.

Not so her husband. He was a venerable and courteous old
gentleman with a long white beard, and had at one time
filled an appointment at the Saxon Court. He was full of funny
stories about the old King's informality, and would insert these
gently when his wife showed signs of flying off the handle.

"Do not mind my wife," he murmured one day when we
were momentarily alone, "she has some of your fiery Scottish
blood in her veins. She does not mean half she says."

Again, like Frau Schmidt, she seemed to consider that her
former British citizenship entitled her to speak more frankly
than politely. All our failings, mental, moral, and spiritual, were
pointed out to me. Our mistakes in diplomacy were dwelt upon
at length, and our unwillingness to understand Germany was
deplored. Nor did certain members of our royal family escape
unscathed.

I bore it all because I knew I was at last hearing what the

Germans were saying to one another about us. Expediency or politeness prevented them from being quite so blunt when talking to the British traveller. After all, they had their carefully nurtured tourist industry to consider.

But I noticed that, as soon as his wife began, the Geheimrat would leave the room. Not ostentatiously, and always with a gently murmured excuse. He must go to keep an appointment at his club . . . he had entirely forgotten to replenish his stock of cigars . . .

"Heil Hitler!" his wife would call after him, rather absurdly, by way of good-bye.

The old man would make a half-turn in order to bow and say, "Auf Wiedersehen!" clearly and firmly.

"I just can't do anything with him," she would tell me, shrugging her shoulders. "Poor old pet, he's a relic of former times. He doesn't seem to be able to orientate himself to our modern Germany at all."

The Geheimrat was a direct descendant of that Böttger who, two hundred and fifty years before, had brought to the Court of Saxony his discovery of the secret of hard paste for porcelain making. The King had promptly taken over the invention and set up his own royal factory at Meissen. Böttger's invention at last enabled the porcelain sent out from it to rival that of Sèvres and to attract the finest designers and colourists. And in this pleasant home on the outskirts of Dresden, one could still examine exquisite groups and decorated pieces from the earliest period of the new invention.

Perhaps that was what chained Herr Böttger to the past and made him allergic to streamlined efficiency. There is nothing streamlined about a Meissen group, nor anything practical either. Those delicate pieces of nonsense spoke, it is true, of a world of privilege. But the privileged then had taste and knowledge. Now, even in spite of Goebbels' Kultur Ministerium, they seemed to have none.

But I had to qualify that first statement after I had inspected the treasures in Dresden's famous Green Vault. Here was shown the huge collection of jewels and bibelots belonging to the Royal House of Saxony. One might examine, under glass, such gems as ostrich eggs mounted in gold, a golden coffee service where the cups were hung on gold spikes protruding from the golden urn ; and the chief treasure of all, the priceless pearls worn by the Queens of Saxony.

They were the size of very large marrowfat peas, and no more beautiful—now. For, as with rare violins, their value was completely destroyed by disuse. They had been unworn for so long that their lustre had vanished. They were what jewellers call "dead" pearls; and as death is always repulsive and frightening, so those large round greyish pebbles stared out of their case in mockery of what they were supposed to be. Enclosed by glass from the air for nearly twenty years, they were now mere valueless, ugly stones.

Frau Schmidt did her best to entertain me. She took me to a film showing the local craftsmen at work. Here one watched crystals from Saxon Switzerland—that tract of mountainous rock between Saxony and Czechoslovakia—being polished and set. It was a special Party performance. I remember, as we came out into the foyer afterwards, her look of satisfaction at seeing so many Party leaders standing around.

"It is good that they see me here," she said, "for they always observe who takes the trouble to attend such organized entertainments."

But it was Elaine who took me to the Bier-Abend which many of the students and others of her friends had organized among themselves. It was a quiet, well-behaved gathering of young people, and they made a point of introducing a young Englishman who was studying German here. He was a lumpish boy who said little but sat glowering with his back to the wall. Every now and then, as one of his friends passed him and made some remark, he would shake himself awake and reply with an odd sort of obsequiousness which affected me unpleasantly.

He had paid no attention to me at all, nor could I discover anything about his background in England. I was therefore surprised to find him walking alongside me when a party of us set off for home. He lingered, to allow the others to get on ahead. Then, turning to me abruptly, he said, "When are you going home to England?"

"Oh, not until autumn. I've a lot to see first."

"I've seen and heard all I want to. If I were you I would go home now."

I was so astonished I halted there on the pavement while the last tram rattled by. "What do you mean?" I asked.

His voice took on an odd note of misery. "I can't tell you—now. I joined one of their beastly student corps, and I've heard enough, I can tell you. I'm frightened. Frightened!"

We had reached the flight of steps leading up to the entry into the Schmidts' block of flats. Elaine had run up before us, and stood waiting for me with her hand on the door. He's had too much beer, I thought. He was standing under the street lamp, and as I turned to say good-bye I saw a look on his face that reminded me of someone else. Not until I was in bed that night did I remember who it was. For the one man was thin and shabbily dressed, and the other a plump, lardy boy. Then it came to me. He reminded me somehow of Mr Smith.

I was disturbed in my mind. For years now, our newspapers had prophesied terrible things, and terrible things had indeed happened. Yet each crisis had passed over, like a cloud passing over a great lake without disturbing its surface. Why should a change of atmosphere in the Pension Schmolke, a few arrogant words from two disenfranchised Englishwomen, and the look on the face of a frightened boy, deter me from rowing a little longer on that lake?

I went next day to say good-bye to the great art collection near the Bruhl Terrace. Many of the pictures had been the private property of the royal family. I stood a long while before a large nineteenth-century conversation-piece showing three young women in crinolines seated at a work-table. The glossy, braided hair, the white necks of two of them, were bent over their embroidery. But the third had half-risen, and was looking over her shoulder as if someone had just entered the room.

I knew the story of that picture. It was a portrait of the three aunts of a Saxon baroness, now herself a middle-aged woman.

It had hung on her grandfather's walls, and had there been, unfortunately, admired by the King. "So," said the little baroness, in mild tones of regret, "my grandfather had, of course, to offer it to his Majesty."

"Why, of course'?" I had asked.

She looked at me in astonishment. "But when the King admired anything, what else could one do but offer it to him?"

I stared at the rich, painted folds of the dresses, and thought perhaps things were the same under the old régime too. Then, to calm my mind, I stepped into the little room where the Sistine Madonna hung in all its glory. No reproduction, however fine, has quite caught the look of inner stillness and wonder in the Madonna's face. I sat for some time on the red velvet bench in front of her. After a while I felt better.

It was my last day in Dresden. I went out on to the Bruhl Terrace and looked down on the river. A great raft of logs was being piloted under the bridge. The magic towers and spires of the city stood up quiet and still in the afternoon air. The people —the trouble-makers, the little ants eating into this beautiful pyramid—were all hurrying home for supper. I knew I would find Dresden's other great glory, the Zwinger, deserted and still.

The fountains had been turned off, and a few leaves were already drifting across their half-empty basins. The Neptune statue turned its cold eyeballs towards me, withholding any advice as to whether to go on or go home. The lovely colonnades stretched in an arc before me, and the rococo pavilions looked more than ever like fantastic dreams made of icing-sugar. Fragile, impermanent though they seemed, they had stood now for more than two hundred years. Like frivolity itself, they were surely indestructible! They gave courage, though in quite another way than had the Sistine Madonna.

The next day I went on to Prague.

24

ONCE the subconscious has become receptive to warning, strange things sometimes happen. Otherwise, I can never quite explain what happened to me in Prague.

A year or two before, a pleasant sensible Dutchwoman, whom I had encountered somewhere or other, had given me the address of a Prague hotel which she could thoroughly recommend. It was not cheap, she had said, but it was quiet and exceedingly good. She herself had stayed in it several times before the First World War which (at the time she told me of it) was not so very far away. It was in the same category as Brown's in London, or the Erzeherzog Rainer in Vienna. That is to say, it was unknown to the average tourist, but very well known indeed to the connoisseur and to the families of the lesser nobility who came to it year after year.

Perhaps the warning had come to me then, and I had not recognized it as such. For of course the "lesser nobility" of those days would be largely Austrians who had been at some time or other granted estates in what was then a province of the old Austrian Empire. And since they kept on coming year after year.... But I never thought of that.

Someone else had given me an introduction to the British Consul at Prague. And the Czech Legation in London had furnished me, not only with letters to the appropriate officials at the Prague Foreign Office but, very handsomely, with a *laissez-passer* for the Customs. Truth to tell, I was so sleepy by the time I reached the frontier that I forgot to produce this last, and had my luggage opened as usual. Although I wasn't trying to smuggle anything through, I felt very bitter about that later.

But now I could see the Czech national colours above the stations, instead of the German. I could remember that I was sitting in a first-class carriage instead of travelling third on a hard wooden bench, as I had done during my former visit to Czechoslovakia. Then I had scarcely started my writing career. I had been going to earn my keep by talking English to an unknown worker in a glass factory in the forgotten carp-pond district of Southern Bohemia. Now I had found my niche as a writer. I could afford to stay in a good hotel, and the publicity department of the Czech Foreign Office had thought me worth while encouraging.

But the journey was long and fatiguing. It was almost midnight before the lights of Prague began to blaze through the carriage window and the train slowed down in the station. My taxi drove me to the hotel. I had developed a nose for hotels, and I saw at once, from its dignified exterior and its quiet, elegantly furnished foyer, that I had come to the right sort of place. The whole of the ground floor formed a lounge, heavily panelled in wood, with shaded lights hanging over the clusters of marble-topped tables. A few late visitors, mostly grey-haired, with an air of shabby distinction, still sat around finishing their drinks.

It was the sort of place where one would get real old-fashioned service, where cocktail bars were unknown, and where the food would be a trifle heavy but good. It was, in short, exactly the kind of place my Dutch friend had said it would be. And I felt suddenly, violently, that I hated it.

While still in the taxi I had heard the chimes strike midnight over the old city. I followed the man who had taken my luggage, and who turned out to be the night-porter, just come on duty. He was elderly, surly, and respectable. I thought he was taking me to the office to register and hand over my passport. But here Providence was with me, though I didn't know it at the time. For the reception clerk had just gone off for the night. The old man was taking me to the lift. And my passport still remained safely in my possession.

He ushered me into my room. It was a charming room with good, old-fashioned furniture and even a wash-stand complete with its array of china equipment. Moss-green velvet curtains covered the windows. When the porter had gone I drew them aside and looked down on the still, wide street with its heavy stone buildings and the moon shining above their roofs. Then I let the curtains swing back again and turned once more to the room.

And I hated it, too. The wash-stand stood staring at me. The great walnut carved bedstead looked as if it were going to swallow me up. The walls appeared to close in, inch by inch. . . . I was in a trap and I knew it. I must get out of this, I said to myself. Tomorrow morning, I must get out!

I undressed and got into bed. I had thought myself too tired even to sleep, but I slept like the dead. I woke up next morning feeling lazy, relaxed, warm as a cat. The green velvet curtains had not been quite drawn together again the night before. A shaft of sunlight flooded the room with its faded pink satin-stripe wallpaper and soft moss-green carpet. Outside, I could hear already the purr of passing cars and the footfalls of people going to their offices early.

What a charming room, I thought to myself, my hands clasped above my head. I remembered the night before, and felt ashamed. Yet I knew that over-fatigue and a migraine headache had often given me such feelings before. All the same, they had been unusually powerful. I hoped it had not been a case of hysteria. . . .

Anyway, everything looked different now. And I would feel even better once I had my morning coffee. So I rang for it. The coffee was strong and black and delicious. The milk came in a small, thin jug which looked as if it might be silver. The crescent rolls, speckled with carraway seed, broke almost at a touch, they were so fresh. I ate one absently, and then looked round for the tray, to put some more butter on the little sharp end of the crescent.

And I got a shock. For the tray was not balanced across my knees, and I was no longer in bed. I was standing, almost completely dressed, putting back everything I had unpacked the night before into my suitcase again. Even while I still wondered at myself, I had clicked down the fasteners and locked the case.

You fool! I told myself, with my finger on the bell. Are you still as mad as you were last night? Do you seriously mean to leave this unique place, with exactly the sort of surroundings you always appreciate, for a regular, streamlined Americanized hotel?

"Bitte, my luggage downstairs. And I shall want a taxi."

It was not quite eight o'clock and the same old night porter had come up. He was indifferent to anything I might choose to do. He did not even know I had booked a room for the whole duration of my stay in the city. But he grumbled a bit about having to make out my bill. It was not his duty, he said. The office clerks should do it, he said, but they did not come into the office till eight. Could I not wait another little minute or two?

No, I could not. And so, without any intention, I left the hotel without being registered there at all, and with my passport still safely in my own possession. But I was just stepping into the taxi when I remembered the British Consul. I had written to him from Dresden the day I left, giving the address of this hotel in case he wished to ring me up.

I knew only of one other; the Hotel President Wilson, near the main station. "If any message comes for me, please say I have gone there," I told the porter, just as the taxi moved off.

It was an ordinary station hotel, large and noisy and too international to be interesting. But my feeling of relief, as I entered it, was almost overpowering. It even made me feel I could do with a second breakfast. After all, I had only eaten one roll and drunk half a cup of coffee, I had been in such a hurry....

The waiter had hardly brought what I ordered when I saw a youngish man standing in the doorway, raking the occupants of the tables with his eye. He looked like an Englishman even from that distance. He spoke to the head waiter who indicated me. Then he came towards me, appearing rather more hurried and agitated than the occasion seemed to demand.

The next moment he stood beside me. Having assured himself that I was the right person, he wasted no time in inquiries as to the health of our mutual friends in London.

"I was expecting you, of course," he said. "The Latimers told me you would be turning up. But I got the shock of my life when your letter came in an hour ago, saying where you were going to stay. I leapt to the phone to warn you to get out. Then I remembered the wires would be tapped, so I didn't."

I stared at him. He didn't seem to notice the stare. He was so flustered he had dropped into the seat opposite me and was busily pouring out some of my coffee into an empty cup. Now, I thought, I can always say I have seen an Englishman looking flustered. . . .

"So I left the telephone alone and called a taxi instead. But when I got there they said you had left already. They told me you were coming here. . . . What about your passport, though! I'm afraid it will have gone to the police. . . ."

"No, it hasn't," I said, and I took it out of my handbag and showed it, explaining about the reception clerk having been off duty.

He actually mopped his head with relief. "You've had amazing luck! But I don't understand. If you knew nothing about that hotel when you arrived, and lit out of it first thing this morning, who tipped you the wink?"

I said, "Will you please tell me what *was* the matter with that hotel? I'll swear it was respectable, anyway. No lovely ladies sitting around with little dogs for gentlemen to pat. No furtive chambermaids——"

"Of course not!" He sounded impatient. "But I'd like very much to know who informed you that it was the secret headquarters of the Sudeten German Party. . . ."

"Of the——"

"Oh, you must have found out somehow or you wouldn't have left it like that! The present owner is a former Austrian landowner, and all his little friends come and stay there regularly. They're just the type to make trouble for the government here—those dispossessed people do. Actually, I knew the hotel was being watched. One more bit of trouble in Sudetenland, and it's sure to be raided——"

"You mean, it might have happened with me in it?" I gaped.

"There would have been that risk. What was sure, though, was that if you hadn't had extraordinary good luck in timing, you'd have been registered now, as staying there. You've got 'journalist' on your passport, haven't you? And I dare say you're looking to the Press Department of the Foreign Office to help you during your stay in the country? I thought so. Well, what sort of help d'you think they'd give a travelling journalist who was apparently hand in glove with the Party that's making all the trouble here? Britishers don't generally know even of that hotel's existence. They'd think your going there mighty suspicious!"

"Well," I said, drawing a breath of relief (for I hadn't, then, been hysterical after all), "I had not the slightest idea of all this."

He cocked an unbelieving eye at me. "Then why did you leave in a hurry?"

"I can't explain it," I said. "I just didn't like the place. I felt I was being—watched."

"So you probably were," he said grimly. "You were a stranger—not an habituée. I'd like to know, though—however, if you don't want to give someone away, I shan't press for an answer."

I did not protest any more. For I saw he was convinced that somebody in the hotel itself must have given me a friendly warning. And I didn't want the impossible task of convincing him, in turn, that nothing but a strong instinct had saved me from blotting my copy-book with the Foreign Office in Prague.

They were business-like there and helpful. They showed me old palaces and new schools. Everyone went about their affairs as usual, square-set, capable, badly-dressed. I spent an afternoon with Isadora Duncan's sister Elizabeth; a grey-haired elderly little spinster who electrified me by saying the trouble with Isadora was she had never expressed herself fully enough. . . .

A day or two later I found myself in the train which bore me far from Prague. Far from civilization, too, since I was bound for that part of the great Carpathian Range known as the High

Tatras. For hour upon hour I travelled, threading almost the whole breadth of this, the most important of the Succession States. The towns fell away, and then even the villages. Well-dressed passengers gave way to stolid countryfolk, and then to peasants. The scenery grew wilder; grew dim as the sun went down.

The train reached its terminus and stood still, panting. It was eleven o'clock at night. A few old-fashioned gas-lamps illu-minated the station. Under one of them I saw standing another of those patient, motionless figures which had been visible at each station for the last hour or so. The figure of a Jew in kaftan and ear-locks, hoping to make some money exchange for a traveller from the West.

Even in the half-obscurity of the station he saw me at once. He came forward, stooping, with the age-old Shylock gesture. Being a Jew, he understood a few words of German. I explained haltingly what I wanted. Not money, for I had enough Czech crowns already, but information as to the next step in the journey.

There was a piece of paper in my purse, crumpled and re-folded a dozen times. I had shown it as often, to fellow travel-lers, hoping they might tell me what next to do, once I had reached the last station on the line. But they had all shaken their heads politely and handed it back. STARY SMOKOVEC, said the paper, and (under the name of what I had been told was a mountain halt) that of the hotel I was bound for— TATRA-HEIM.

I handed the paper to the Jew. He took it between long, dirty fingers, peering at the words. Then suddenly his cloak of meek patience vanished. He shouted violently at the one porter, who had been unable to understand what I wanted and who was standing, bewildered, with my luggage at his feet. The Jew's arm shot out from his long, cloaklike garment, seizing mine. I felt myself dragged along towards the station entrance. Dragged through it, into the middle of the dark square, and thrust into a fantastic conveyance, half tram, half funicular, which travelled along lines lying like a coiled serpent through the very heart of the town.

I was only half-through the lighted aperture when the tram moved forward. My luggage was hurled after me, and the guard caught hold of me, steadying me into a seat. I flung some money, haphazard, through the window and saw the Jew and the porter dive for it simultaneously. Then almost at once, it seemed, the lit windows of the township vanished, and we were travelling through the dark.

Where? To this place Stary Smokovec which someone in Prague had told me about? I was too tired to care. Now and then a musical horn would blow from somewhere, and the door in the middle of the long, snakelike compartment would open. But there were no lights now, only darkness outside the lighted coach. Somebody would get out, and the thing would move on again.

The door slid open once more. The guard was shaking my shoulder. The next moment he was leaning out and dropping my two suitcases into the void. I climbed down the steps and stood for a moment still warmed by the yellow lights of the coach. Then they began to withdraw from me, to rise higher into the air as the car went on upward and vanished round a bend.

I stood there in the dark. Presently, as my eyes got accustomed to it, the lid of the dark began to appear deep blue, sprinkled with stars. Boulders and stones near me gradually took on shape. And I could see that there must be a wood on the other side of the path I was standing on, because a little light showed between the tree trunks, emphasizing their height and blackness.

But it was only the light of a mountain night. There was no glimmer of any house light around. I stood very still, beginning to be afraid. When one is afraid, one's ears take charge. Mine strained so, I became, as the saying is, all ears. And the first thing I heard was the fall of a little cascade just beside me. I turned round to look at it. I could just make out the grey water falling down a sort of bank, into a basin beneath.

The basin was not natural, it had been made by hand. Nor was the flight of carved steps in the rock beside it natural. My ears went back into place. I picked up my suitcases, climbed the rock steps, and at the top saw immediately what had been hidden from the road below.

There stood Tatra-Heim, in all the sugar-icing flamboyance of a once-fashionable mountain hotel. I could see the fretted balconies beneath each window, and (here and there only, for it must be now past midnight) a thread of light showing between the shutters. The cascade had fallen from a little stream which ran down one side of the formal gardens. The asphalt path ran straight and dark towards the front door. I walked up to it and rang the bell.

A sleepy waiter opened the door, seized my cases without comment, and beckoned me to follow. We passed up a wide staircase, down a long corridor covered with brown matting, and then he ushered me into my room, bowed, and shut the door. It was a dull and shabby little room, but there were glass doors leading on to the balcony.

I flung them wide. Instantly the ice-cold mountain air blew in. I stepped on to the balcony and saw the jagged teeth of the mountains towering above me. Not only the cascade, but the sound of other mountain streams began to make themselves audible through the night. And above them, and all the other little chattering noises of the mountain-side, there was the cold silence of the stars.

Part Six

TATRA-HEIM

25

THE High Tatras divide Slovakia from Poland, and this was the Slovakian side. Since Slovakia itself had been a province of Hungary before the war, the Tatra Mountain resorts had been planned to please the rich Hungarian tourist. But now the Hungarians stayed at home, angry and contemptuous of this new state carved out of the former possessions of the old Empire. The Czechs had built other holiday resorts elsewhere along the Tatras, with hotels like cigar-boxes and everything streamlined and modern. And the old-fashioned hotels, designed to please the taste of the Magyar aristocracy, languished, half-empty.

It was in one of these that I found myself. The downstairs rooms were grandiose in the extreme, at the expense of the bedrooms, which no one except their owners saw. This must have been to satisfy the Magyar love of an impressive façade. But I would have preferred less gold stucco around the pillars in the hall and more carpeting on my bedroom floor. The great dining-room was decorated with that favourite Magyar combination —chocolate and gold. Chocolate cherubs hung like captured flies from the ceiling, and the gold mirrors reflected both the mountains outside and the acre of empty tables within.

Of course, it was the end of the season. But the Austrian General's wife confided to me that there had been plenty of vacant tables even at its height. "Indeed, it is to be feared that Frau Schwarzova will soon have to close down. Her clientele was built up before the war, among those who have now no money to travel. I only come here because my health requires it, and because she is good enough to make an Arrangement. But how long will it last?"

The Frau General was a tall woman with an imposing bust. Her grey hair was swept up into a pre-war pompadour, and

she made no concessions to modern fashion. Still, there was a
stately elegance about her which forced everyone to cede her
first place in the social hierarchy of the hotel. She had taken
under her wing a pretty, pale young Hungarian girl called
Erzhebet whose parents in Budapest had managed to scrape
up enough money to send their daughter away for a dose of
good mountain air.

"Come, Erzhebet!" The words always preceded a move by
the Frau General from one room to another, or from indoors to
out. They were uttered in kindly tones of command, echoing
through the empty hall. The next moment one would see the
Frau General descending the staircase, alpenstock in hand, felt
hat decorated with chamois brush on the back of her head, and
a dim figure following behind her. Or perhaps she was merely
moving from the front salon with the view of the mountains
to the back with the crackling stove. Then Erzhebet would be
carrying the Frau General's large knitting-bag containing the
half-hoop of metal on which she cast stitches instead of on
needles. And together they would disappear like a mighty ship
with a little tug in attendance.

Pani Schwarzova, who ran the hotel, had obviously once
been Frau Schwarz but, lacking the Frau General's strength of
will (besides, the Frau General lived in Vienna), had thought it
politic to Slavicize her name. She was a lean, anxious woman
with ingratiating manners and a skin touched with the yellow
of Jewish or Magyar blood. She was fond of telling me about
the Good Days, when not only was the dining-room full at
every meal from May to October, but she could even afford to
engage a small orchestra for the season.

"The Frau General was a young woman then. Ach! Wie
Schön! Like Brunhilde, as she strode in to dinner in front of
her man, who was only a Captain when they began to come
here first. I suppose officers behave differently when on the field
of battle, but certainly she had the greater habit of command...."

There were other shadowy figures slipping in and out of the
hotel or occupying corners of the vast dining-room, where they

talked together in whispers; but only the Frau General had
enough personality to conquer the space and silence of decay.
Her orders rang cheerfully through the room, when others in-
stinctively lowered their voices because of its echo. I did myself.
But then, she had been coming for years and years. For long
enough to appropriate the dining-room as her own, as well as to
make an Arrangement.

Whether the others were Czechs, Hungarians, or Germans, I
never knew. They did not speak loudly enough for me to find
out. But a couple from Northern Germany did turn up, on a
walking tour through the Carpathians. Both husband and wife
bulged with muscles, and were never seen without large green
knapsacks which they even brought in to dinner, letting them
fall with a thud on the floor so that, in the silence, everyone
jumped.

They stayed only a week-end, and came into the little salon,
the one where the stove was lit, on Sunday evening. With bows
of apology they seated themselves at a round table covered
with green plush. They opened before them a large, expensive
book of photographed mountain scenes. I had looked at the
book myself, in the one souvenir shop still open, farther down
the line at Tatranska Lomnitza. It was too expensive for me.
But I knew that the captions under each picture were printed
in Czech, Slovak, and Hungarian.

The wife took out a pencil and held it above the first page.
With another bow, her husband addressed Erzhebet. Would
the young Hungarian lady be kind enough to translate, so that
they might obtain the correct description of each scene? Erzhebet, fluttered at being brought into the limelight, looked over
their shoulders, dictating slowly in German. The place-names
were the same in both languages, and I should have thought
that the pictures explained themselves. But under an obvious
sunset scene I watched the German woman carefully transcribe,
"Now Day Sinks into the Arms of Night," and then proceed to
copy each flowery sentence, page by page.

When they had bowed once more and retired with satisfied

expressions, I raised my eyebrows in the Frau General's direction.

"My dear young lady," she said at once, "that was an exhibition of North German thoroughness! You and I can recognize a photograph of a sunset, nicht? In Vienna we have more to do with our time!"

Each morning, after my coffee and roll, I would walk out, through the formal garden which so badly required to be filled up with figures of pre-war elegance, and passed down the flight of rock steps on to the winding road. The rails of the tram-funicular glinted down the middle of it, vanishing round the bend. If I wanted to, I would take it back down the slope as far as Tatranska Lomnitza, which had been a fashionable resort in its day.

Even now, there were no fewer than three hotels open. They boasted the same elaborate Edwardian architecture as the Hôtel Tatra-Heim, and just as few guests. The man who kept the souvenir shop used to watch out hopefully for me at first, but with disillusion as time went on. I would enter the largest hotel, order coffee, and drink it in the same gold and chocolate surroundings as those from which I had come. The same elderly relics of a vanished régime sat about reading Viennese or Budapest newspapers several days old. And I was conscious that the Czechs, who now owned this side of the mountains, were having what they, in their dictionary English, would no doubt call a merry time, in brighter cafés and restaurants elsewhere. But where?

The only Czech institution within reach of Tatra-Heim was the Sanatorium Dr Hrusa. It took me some days to come across it, and then only because I had walked farther than usual. For I soon tired of catching the funicular downwards towards Tatranska, and now, in the mornings, crossed the tram rails instead and took the footpath through the woods.

There were only sparse handfuls of trees which grew here and there in pockets of soil. I was above the real forests, among the huge masses of rock which went up sheer into the blue air. The sides of the mountains were bare and menacing. There was not the softness of the Tyrolean Alps nor the glittering snow of Switzerland. Here were only precipices of granite and sandstone over which there occasionally winged the shadow of some giant bird.

Occasionally a waterfall or patch of green made an oasis, near which ran the path marked out for walkers. I had found one of those green clefts, where the trees momentarily shut out the terrible mountains. One might imagine oneself in a miniature valley. The little stream sang between banks of moss, and a few late blueberries showed under their creeper-like plants. I sat down by the stream for a while. The water was brown and clear. Some child had built a water-wheel near a ridge of stones over which the stream fell in a tiny cascade. The same child must have been sailing a paper boat, for I saw the battered and folded wreck of it sticking with its nose in the bank. Idly I drew it out. It had words scrawled on it, but the water had blurred them so that I could not make out even the language in which they were written.

I got up and moved away from the stream. Here, outside this small strip of greenery, the path seemed to have been widened. There was even a seat farther on. When I reached the seat I caught sight of a huge square building perched on a ledge with SANATORIUM DR HRUSA painted in black letters right across it. The frontage of the building was honeycombed with balconies. But the balconies were high and solid, almost like little outside rooms lacking roofs. They blocked the windows entirely, so that I could see nothing behind them at all.

I had lingered in the green patch, and sat resting upon the seat, until now it was suddenly cold. The mountains grew sharper against the sky. Far below me the valley seemed to be growing dark already. Some of Dr Hrusa's patients must have thought night was creeping upon them, or merely wanted to raise their spirits, for a faint yellow glow began to make itself visible above the rim of a few of the balconies, as if hands had been outstretched within the last few minutes to switch on electric lamps. . . .

By the time I got back to the hotel it was really dark. But now my eyes had grown accustomed to the slate-grey line of the path leading to it, and I had found my way without difficulty. Pani Schwarzova scolded me when she saw me come in. She felt my coat, which was wet with dew.

"A very dangerous thing to do," she told me reprovingly. "Where has the Pani been walking?"

"As far as the Sanatorium Dr Hrusa."

"The poor souls in there! It is their last step before heaven."

26

THE Slovak maid who brought me my breakfast lingered by the door instead of going away as usual.

"Pani Schwarzova goes to Kesmark to do some shopping. She has ordered a car. She says, would you like to come too?"

Kesmark was a German town which lay in the Slovak valley at the foot of the mountains. There were sixteen of those towns scattered around the province of Zips. They had been founded and settled long ago by emigrants from Germany proper, whose descendants, known as Zipsers, still lived in them, using the old German town laws and speech. I had long wished to visit one of these towns, and snatched at the opportunity to see the nearest, in which Pani Schwarzova did her shopping.

It was curious to slide down the mountain slope in a hired car from the railway terminus, instead of by the funicular-tram. I kept catching my breath as the car seemed to leave the rails. To pass through Tatranska Lomnitza without stopping made one somehow feel superior. It was the first car I had seen, let alone travelled in, since I came. Fashion had left that stretch of the High Tatras, and the big tourist cars always followed fashion.

"I hire this car from Poprad once a week," Pani Schwarzova told me; adding with a sigh, "formerly the hotel had its own bus, which also fetched the supplies from Kesmark. But now no longer."

The Tatra Mountains rise so sheer from the plain at their feet that, once one is within the range, they seem higher and farther above level ground than they are. One moment it seemed we were travelling between walls of rock suspended half-way towards the sky, the next minute one wall of rock had fallen behind, displaying the Slovak Plain at our feet.

We had been among blue shadows, cold air and waterfalls. Now we looked down on a stretch of agricultural land, golden as a carpet, still and sun-baked from the long summer. Right in the middle, like a toy township laid out by a child, was Kesmark. Its houses had red, sloping roofs which at this distance above them looked tightly packed together and pierced in the middle by a church steeple stabbing upwards like a giant darning-needle. Doll-like figures moved about the little gardens behind the houses. Across the reaped fields outside the town one could make out a few geese, mere greyish dots moving erratically over the stubble.

The car nosed downward. Almost at once the chill began to go out of the air. By the time we reached the level of the plain, which seemed in a very few minutes, Pani Schwarzova and I had both wriggled out of our coats. The mountain road had been flinty and innocent of dust. Now puffs of brown dust blew up from under the wheels, and we had to close the windows again in spite of the heat.

A herd of cattle came towards us, moving head downward through a creeping balloon of dust. Their bodies brushed past the car which had slowed to a crawl, and the small boy driving them from behind blew away the lock of hair falling over his eyes in order to stare at us better. By the time we had passed the cows we were already in the centre of the town. There stood the wide market-place before us, lined with carts tilted backwards, their shafts in the air. The fruit and vegetables they had brought into Kesmark (for this was market-day) were already ranged on the stalls; live chickens tied together in bunches like heaving feather mops, yellow mounds of sugar melons, butter, and eggs. Pani Schwarzova got out of the car and moved down the stalls, sharp-eyed. After a few minutes I tired of listening to her bargaining, and left her to visit the church.

Its outside was not so extraordinary, but inside it was unique. For the roof and walls were almost entirely covered with intricate wood-carving which festooned the whole place like brown lace. Pierced filigree carving dripped from the pillars and swarmed up towards the window arches. The altar and pulpit writhed with it, and, as the natural colour of the wood had been kept, the whole church was snuff-coloured inside and smelt like the interior of a blanket chest.

The effect was almost alarming. Delicate and beautiful as the carving was, it had not been subordinated to any architectural plan. One could imagine each German emigrant claiming so many yards of space, taking his chisel in hand, and determining to work out his own invention to the glory of God and his own particular skill.

The air seemed full of an invisible powder that blew up one's nose. I sneezed, tiptoed carefully out of the church in case any vibration should loosen one of the enormous swags of wooden embroidery and bring it down on my head, and entered the market-square again. There stood the Landesbanke at the corner; the shops with their German names above them; and the men and women dressed in heavy, old-fashioned clothes but disdaining the beautiful Slovak costume of the villages round about, carrying their racial superiority wrapped round them like an invisible cloak.

"I think I have now bought all we require," said Pani Schwarzova, moving towards the car, followed by the chauffeur, who was carrying a large basket of eggs. This time we had both to squeeze into the front seat beside the driver, because the back of the car was piled high with fruit, vegetables, the carcasses of one or two fowls, and a sack of meal. The mountains stood sharply in front, not showing themselves behind gentle foothills as in most places, but rising like veiled figures straight from the ground. Nearer they came, as if they had begun to walk towards us.

"Now we must put on our coats," said Pani Schwarzova as they suddenly cut off the sun.

Yet, once one had climbed to the rocky ledges and heights, the sun beat down warmly enough. There lay the hidden lakes, called Eyes of the Sea, so high and remote that they sparkled alone and undisturbed by all save the toughest walkers. In such wild scenery it was easy to believe the tales one was told about brigands. Pani Schwarzova assured me that nowadays there

were none. But not so long before the mountain caves had given
shelter to political refugees from the Polish or Hungarian sides
of the mountains. And these men were forced to take to
brigandage for a living.

It seemed to have been an aristocratic sort of brigandage, all
the same, and more on the lines of Robin Hood than anything
else. Many of the brigands bore noble names and had been
patriotic rebels against the Habsburgs. They robbed the rich
and gave to the poor. A glamorous aura now hung over these
names, especially that of Janacek the Dancer. From his very
name he must have been a Slovak and therefore a peasant. But
ballads and local tradition describe him as tall, handsome, and
very gallant. His delight was in dancing, and he would run any
risks to attend some festivity. He ran one too many, and was
captured in one of the Zipser towns, where he had gone to enjoy
a great ball. Tradition further states that he danced all the way
to the scaffold.

Every morning now, I found I had to climb higher and
higher to get any warmth from the sun. The stove in the back
salon was stuffed with brushwood quite early each afternoon,
and lit well before dinner. The Czech officers had departed; the
vague, anonymous figures that had come for a night or two
now came no longer. And a whole floor of the hotel had been
carefully cleaned and shut up already.

It was the end of the season. There remained in the hotel
only myself, the Frau General, Erzhebet her young Hungarian
shadow, and a noisy group of students from Prague who were
leaving at the end of the week. In fact, we were all leaving
quite soon, and no one anticipated the arrival of the Woman
in the Fur Coat.

But we saw her get off the funicular-tram while we were
having our after-luncheon coffee on the terrace. At midday the
terrace still caught the sun, and though the autumn flowers in
the garden looked rather nipped, they made a brave show if
one did not look too closely. For days now, we had been used to
the funicular rattling past without stopping, with a sharp ring
of its bell as it rounded the corner hiding the last "halt" high up

the mountain-side. When the noise suddenly stopped, we all raised our heads in surprise.

"A new arrival at this season?" the Frau General exclaimed, her eyes glued to the top of the steps. One could never actually see the funicular because of the steep bank hemming the garden in from the road. New arrivals always materialized suddenly, appearing like jack-in-the-boxes at the top of the steps.

Now, as suddenly, we all saw a tall, slim woman poise herself on the edge of the bank, where the path began, and then walk swiftly along it towards us. Most visitors, however *mondaine*, would modify their dress and appearance when coming to such an out-of-the-world place as this. She had not. Her make-up was that of a townswoman, and her fur coat was of summer ermine slung carelessly like a cloak over her shoulders.

The hotel entrance swallowed her up. We looked at each other, amazed. Behind us, through the glass doors leading back to the dining-room, there began to be a certain activity. Erzhebet got up from her chair and looked. She reported that Pani Schwarzova herself was setting food out on one of the tables. Now (Erzhebet said) the woman in the fur coat had sat down and was eating. But she did not take time to eat much, for in a very few minutes the glass doors opened, and she walked on to the terrace smoking a cigarette.

We waited for the Frau General to address the stranger first. "A beautiful day!" she said, looking up blandly from her knitting. "Has the lady travelled from far?"

"All night," was the reply, given shortly, in German with a strong Hungarian accent.

"Ah. From Budapest?"

The stranger nodded. "The express was late, so I missed the morning funicular. Can you please tell me——?"

"But your luggage? You did not lose it, I hope?"

The stranger indicated her large, expensive crocodile bag. "I have no luggage. I came away in such a hurry.... All I require is in this. Will you be good enough to tell me how I can reach the Sanatorium Dr Hrusa?"

The Frau General drew in her breath sharply. Then she gave

a reluctant order to Erzhebet. "Erzhebet, go! You know my lameness prevents my walking so far...."

Unfortunately she had turned her ankle in coming downstairs that morning. Otherwise nothing would have prevented her from accompanying the stranger, and finding out all about her on the way. As it was, she gave meaning looks towards Erzhebet to do so for her. But (as she complained to me afterwards) the girl was too stupid. Not only did she fail to fish up one single concrete fact, but she even allowed herself to be dismissed long before the Sanatorium was reached. Indeed, she came trailing back to us a bare half-hour after setting forth.

"She said she could manage the rest of the way alone. Jesus-Maria, what must that coat have cost?"

"Thou didst not even find out what patient she was visiting?"

Erzhebet shook her head humbly.

"Very well. One thing I am sure of. If he is a man, he is not her husband. Otherwise there would have been none of this unseemly impatience. They must have sent her a wire from the Sanatorium, and she just stepped into the train as she was. Such clothes, for a place like this!"

Balked curiosity made the Frau General's tongue sharper than usual. The bandaged ankle was another cause of frustration, and a third was the disappearance of Pani Schwarzova, who did not appear, as usual after the arrival of each new visitor, to let herself be pumped.

"Ashamed, that's that she is. Ashamed to confess that she is putting up a woman like that. An actress at least, but probably worse. Didst thou notice her walk? It had that studied enticement.... But perhaps Pani Schwarzova will come out and join us over our coffee...."

However, she didn't. The afternoon coffee and cakes (an extra on the bill) was brought out by the Slovak girl at four o'clock. By then the sun was beginning to slide behind the mountains, and we all felt we wanted our coats. Erzhebet said she would collect them and bring them down.

An idea came to the Frau General. "Drink thy coffee quickly

Erzhebet, Liebchen! It is still pleasant enough for thee to enjoy a stroll to the Sanatorium. Then thou canst escort the poor one home, for who knows what bad news may have awaited her there?"

But Erzhebet, curiously enough, dug in her heels.

"She will think I am following her if I come out alone. She will think——"

"Then take our English friend with thee."

I had no option but to put on my coat and set out. The sun still shone on the path, but every now and then, where we stepped through the shadow of some giant rock, the air turned icily cold. By the time we had reached the small plateau with its stream and oasis of greenery, we were both anxious to thread it as quickly as possible and get into the sunshine again.

But it was just here that we met the woman in the fur coat. She stepped into the cold green shadow of the trees from the path which led towards the Sanatorium. Her face was in shadow too, and one could not read her expression. So as to avoid seeming to have come out specially to meet her, Erzhebet paused by the stream and gazed down, with apparent interest, at the small water-wheel.

The woman stood beside us, looking at it too.

I said, "I think some child must come here to play. The last time I came here, there was a paper boat stuck in the bank."

"Why," Erzhebet stared at me, "don't you know who makes those paper boats? There isn't any child up here within miles. No, it is the patients from Dr Hrusa's Sanatorium; the ones who are well enough to walk this distance, of course."

The woman wrapped her fur coat more tightly about her. "Why do they do that? They are ill, of course, but not childish or imbecile!"

Erzhebet looked confused. "Oh, it is a game they play. . . ."

The other glanced at her sharply. "What game?"

"They write their own names on the boats. Then they watch if the boats manage to sail as far as that bend without sticking in the bank. If they do, they—the names written on them—are going to get well."

"And if they don't? Thank you, you need not explain."

Erzhebet stood there looking very uncomfortable. It had been an unfortunate subject to discuss with anyone who had obviously come direct from the Sanatorium. I suppose I should have broken the painful moment by leaving the side of the stream and making the others follow. But I was watching what the stranger was doing.

She had drawn an old envelope out of her beautiful crocodile bag. Her long, nervous fingers had twisted it into a cocked hat or little boat, whichever you liked to call it. She flattened it momentarily on the palm of one hand, so as to scribble something across it with the pencil pulled out of her bag. Then she knelt down and launched the boat.

Neither Erzhebet nor I could move now. We were frozen by the emotion of the woman who stood beside us. We felt her tenseness in our own muscles. We watched with her eyes as the gay little boat bobbed down the middle of the stream, sometimes veering dangerously from one side to the other, but always, so far, righting itself. . . .

Suddenly her control snapped. The little boat was still some way from the bend in the stream, when she began running alongside, and when she drew level she walked right into the water, in her transparent silk stockings and crocodile shoes, and grabbed it up. Dripping, she splashed her way back, and then, standing there on the bank, she rolled the sodden piece of paper into a ball and threw it savagely into the bushes.

"A stupid, stupid game!"

We walked home practically in silence, with only Erzhebet making a timid remark now and then. How long the woman in the fur coat stayed at Hôtel Tatra-Heim, I don't know. For I left myself the next morning.

27

WHEN I entered the Pension Schmolke again, I knew it would be for the last time.

Everything had changed too much. Frau Schmolke herself had changed, even in her physical appearance. She was no longer as tall and commanding. She seemed to have fallen in and down. The long ear-rings she wore, no longer swung cheerfully, they drooped. And I could not bear to see the marks of worry and distress on her face. Worry on account of the poorer quality of the food she was obliged to give her guests. "Butter is very short, I am really ashamed. One small pat to everyone only! But they say the hospitals require it. . . ." Worry on account of the difficulty of getting help. And a deeper worry too, etching its lines on her face and turning her quite suddenly into an old woman.

I could not bear to see Gertrud Orff's efforts to avoid me. She avoided me because she was ashamed, and, because she was ashamed, she had become hard-voiced and dogmatic. I didn't like Herr Holz's expression much, either. Nor the small-mindedness with which he pressed me to discover that Sir Thomas Beecham had Aryan German blood in him somewhere.

"Think, Fräulein. He *must*! Perhaps a grandmother, or even a great-grandmother of whom you know nothing? For he is (I must say it) a really first-class musician!"

Well, anyway, he had admitted that a Britisher could be that.

The Pole had gone back suddenly to Poland. Her decision had made everyone surprised and thoughtful. There was no reason for it, Frau Schmolke had protested; no reason at all. She had as many pupils as she could take, even during the summer, and the prospect of one or two concert engagements in the autumn. Besides, the Colonel had gone. All the officers were away on manœuvres, now that the harvest was in and they could tramp about the fields and put up barbed wire and so on.

"Did she give any reason for leaving?" I asked.

Before Frau Schmolke could reply, Herr Holz did. "She announced that her country needed her! Those Poles live on high-flown notions. If there exists no situation about which they can feel romantic, they immediately create one."

We had reached the fag-end of summer. Most of the tourists had gone home, and the *pension* was comparatively empty. But the day after I came there arrived an Italian family, father, mother, daughter, and son. Frau Schmolke could tell us nothing about them, except that they had written for rooms. We all asked her separately and privately, for none of us could make them out.

They were a respectable lower-middle-class family. Respectability was indeed the key-note. They sat, tight and prim, in their places at meals, speaking little, for they knew practically no German, and evidently thought it impolite to converse in Italian among themselves. Although it was still exceedingly hot, their notions of dress were propriety itself. Father wore a thick black suit with a high collar and very white cuffs. Mother wore buttoned dresses right up to her throat, the like of which I had not seen in recent years except in enlarged photographs. Daughter wore print dresses, whose modest opening at the neck was always secured by a silver brooch showing the Virgin's head. Her sleeves came down well below the elbow and, even to her parents, she never spoke until she was spoken to.

The son wore a tight navy blue suit, very shiny with use, but very well brushed. His hair, glossy and black with oil, shone like a mirror. He was about sixteen, with the first faint down of a moustache on his upper lip. He sat, silent and respectful between his parents, saying, "Si, Papa" or "Si, Mama" as spoken to. He leapt to open doors for his mother, and was never seen to go out without the rest of his family.

"But they all go around together in a bunch," Paul said to me, while we were discussing the enigma of the Italian family. "And what they do with themselves, I can't think. I speak some

Italian and I've been trying to talk to them. They haven't been out to Potsdam, they haven't bothered about any of the sights. And when I recommended the opera, they said they were always busy in the evenings."

"For tourists, they don't seem to be enjoying themselves much," I suggested.

"They're not ordinary tourists, anyway. I know Italy, and I can place them bang off. Peasant stock obviously, or perhaps the owners of the little shop in some out-of-the-way place or other. All that correctitude belongs to the type. Have you noticed the girl and boy are never allowed out alone? No, Papa or Mama or both go out too, to chaperon. You find the custom surviving only in the top crust of peasant respectability."

"I shouldn't have thought they'd have money enough to travel."

"That's another thing. They never go out of their own province, these people, as a rule. It's an occasion if they visit a farm ten miles off. As for going to see a foreign country, well, they wouldn't dream of it for an instant, no matter how well filled the family stocking!"

At least Paul, the gay young Hungarian pianist, had not changed. On my last visit he had been away, making a concert tour in England. He had turned up just after I arrived, to be greeted almost with tears of joy by Frau Schmolke.

"I thought thou wouldst be too grand for this simple establishment now that thou art winning an international reputation! The Hungarians are so fond of the English too. . . . I thought I had lost thee for good!"

He patted her on the shoulder. "But you and I must stick together! Never let it be said that Hungary and Germany have drifted apart!"

He winked at me over her shoulder. But I caught a smug gleam behind Herr Holz's shining spectacles.

Everything in the city seemed a little dusty and dead. The opera-houses were closed and the concert season not yet begun. Nicolai's place was empty at table too. He had written to me to say that he had decided to accept an offer to sing bass in a small opera-house in a little town near the Baltic coast. So small was the town, I had never heard of it, and was surprised that, even in Germany, it could rise to a permanent opera company.

"So he gave up his dream of going to Australia at last?" I was discussing the matter with Frau Schmolke. Nicolai's letter had made no mention of Australia at all. It was the letter of a man who had lost hope.

She shrugged her shoulders. "It was only a dream, poor fellow! When the offer came, I did my best to persuade him to accept. The salary is small, but a single young man can at least live on it. And he will get much experience that way."

"I think its proximity to Danzig helped him to decide," Paul added quietly.

"Danzig?"

"It's quite a big port. One can get over to Scandinavia easily in an emergency, even on a Nansen Passport."

Herr Holz, who had been listening, looked annoyed.

I was strolling along the Unter den Linden, wondering if I should look in at Braun's and get a new hat, when I saw coming towards me a brisk figure I recognized. It was the Baron from Riga. He was elegantly dressed and looked on top of the world. When he saw me he raised his grey felt and stopped.

"My dear lady, but how delightful to encounter you here! Let us step into this café and drink to this unexpected occasion!"

We sat down and he gave the order. "How is the Professor?" I asked.

An impatient look came over his face. "She has got a little excitable. It seems that she does not like the way things are going in Europe. Her conversation at meals really gets more tactless and outspoken every day. I fear that before next winter I shall have to make other domestic arrangements."

"I don't like the way things are going in Europe myself," I said. "I used to be happy in Germany, but there are a lot of things one hears about that I don't like at all."

"Tush!" he said briskly. "One can't make an omelet without breaking eggs."

Now he was looking displeased. Weakly, I hastened to propitiate him by changing the subject. "Are you taking a holiday in Berlin?"

"Partly. And partly I am here to attend a conference held by the Latvian Balts. We have formed a little society in Riga, you know. It began by being merely a social club, where we could speak our own language together and keep up old contacts between friends. But naturally, we had our political aims as well, and we find sympathetic encouragement here."

An air of satisfaction had taken the place of the rather peevish criticism in which he used to indulge when we were alone. The climate of the Unter den Linden seemed to agree with him. I said good-bye when we left the café, and after giving me a sweeping bow, with the pearl-grey felt hat in his hand, he swung off to meet some of his friends at the Adlon.

I met Paul in the corridor of the Pension Schmolke. He dragged me into the little telephone room. "Listen! It's such a good joke, I can't wait till evening. . . . You know those Italians? Well, I've discovered what they're doing in Berlin!"

I held my breath. Was it possible that they had come here for the same purpose, more or less, as the Baron? Something to do with Italy and Germany. . . . Then I remembered the mild and stuffy look of the whole family and decided that I must be going mad.

Paul was hissing in my ear. "They're circus acrobats!"

"No!" I felt unaccountably relieved. "How did you find out?"

"Saw them doing their act last night. I had a free night—didn't want to do any more practice before my recital in case I got stale. So I went along to the performance, just to relax my mind. You ought to see Papa wearing nothing but a leopard skin balancing the trapeze and his family at the same time!"

I burst out laughing.

"*That's* why they're so abominably correct. Apart from their upbringing in village propriety, I've always heard that circus folk observe *les convenances* more strictly than anyone."

When Frau Schmolke heard the news she looked oddly pleased. "My house has always attracted artists," she said, "and to work the trapeze act takes that balance and self-control which I am always begging dear Paul to develop more strongly."

Now, at meal-times, we gazed respectfully across at the acrobatic family, noting how discreetly they ate and how moderately they drank. They never mentioned their profession, so we did not mention it either. I always meant one night to go and see them for myself, in their leopard skins and tights. But I procrastinated as usual. And one day they were not at table. Their act was finished. They had moved on elsewhere.

Part Seven

THE BOUQUET WELL

28

I HAD known it was time for me to move on too; but I felt a reluctance to recross the Channel while the fine weather lasted. Berlin might be hot and dusty, but elsewhere surely one might be able to breathe. I had heard one of the guests at the *pension* talk of a little spa in the less-known part of Hanover. It was a cheap little place, patronized almost entirely by Germans. Its description brought up confused memories of two books; Katherine Mansfield's *In a German Pension* and—more far-away—Beatrice Harraden's old best-seller, *Ships that Pass in the Night*.

So I wrote and booked a room at the Hôtel Edelweiss in Bad Nenndorf.

The wide, reaped fields lay all around it, and, beyond, the dark pine forests. At its core was a beautiful little park whose prim flower-beds, groomed to a hair, were glowing already with autumn colour. In the middle of the park was the Bath House. It had a conservatory with wicker chairs placed under the palms so that one could await one's turn if too early, or fill up one's time when waiting for a friend who was getting treatment.

I would drop in myself, to watch plump husbands wait for their wives or vice versa; and the gentle rustle of greenery was matched by the rustle of turned-over newspapers. Now and then a bath-woman would appear to summon someone or other. The bath-women all wore the local costume, one of the very few in all Europe which could be called truly ugly. Yet the ugliness did not lie in the long rustling skirts, it lay in the hair-dressing. An enormous bun was coiled right above, and dipping over, the forehead. Not even the loveliest features could conquer that, and the Hanoverian peasant is hard-faced at the best.

The baths themselves were efficacious but primitive. They were contained in cubicles rather like horse-boxes, with no frills by way of polished tiling or other concessions to looks. There were the baths of bubbling mineral water, which were very pleasant. And there were the mud-baths, whose curative properties were so strong that few people were allowed to submerge more than the limb in need of treatment.

Few people, in fact, wanted to. For the mud was particularly obnoxious and evil-smelling; and, moreover, there had been a rumour just before my arrival that a hair-pin had been found in one. This might well be a libel, for the whole set-up, though not luxurious, was immaculate and stringently well-ordered. As well it might be, since Bad Nenndorf had been specially taken in hand by the Government to provide a Cure for the humbler members of society, the small tradespeople and those whose means and tastes unfitted them for the more expensive pleasures of Bad Oyenhausen a few miles off.

But, in this little world of routine rambles, meals, and gossip, even a hair-pin made news. I heard it discussed avidly down the long tables of the Hôtel Edelweiss; on park benches while the band played; and, of course, in the Bath House Conservatory itself. The mud should be properly cleansed. It should be cleansed, somehow, after each patient had left it. It should be sifted mechanically, by some machine. Herr Jé, if that were done, what else might not be found?

Presently the hair-pin gave way to something more sensational, something funny this time. The joke rang through all the hotels, was whispered between elderly ladies who sat knitting on the terrace of the restaurant overlooking the park, was told, nudgingly, by old gentlemen reading their papers under the palms while waiting for their wives to finish their treatment. . . .

It appeared that a couple had arrived a few days before, the lady to undergo treatment for rheumatism. They had set out to discover the Bath House, and while crossing the park had encountered a business acquaintance of the husband's. This gentleman had courteously offered to escort his friend's wife to

her treatment and return her afterwards to her hotel, in order
to enable her husband to go back there and finish some business
letters.

He had seated himself with his newspaper in the conservatory while his friend's wife went off for her bath. The lady had
duly been fetched by the grimmest of the rustling bath-women
and introduced to a cubicle containing a bath full of nauseous
black mud. Not grasping as yet what lay before her, she had
undressed and allowed the bath-woman to take her clothes right
out of the cubicle. She had then, in revulsion at the look of the
mud, refused to go into it on any account. . . .

In vain the bath-woman pleaded and scolded. At last, as a
final measure, she had announced, "I go then to fetch your
husband to reason with you." And had left the cubicle before
her tearful patient had been able to explain that the gentleman
who had arrived with her was not, in fact, her husband at all.

He, still reading his newspaper in the steamy and fragrant air
of the great glass-house, looked up to find the bath-woman
standing beside him. "Please to follow me," she commanded,
and obediently he got up and followed her.

Meanwhile the naked woman in the cubicle heard two pairs
of footsteps approaching, one manly. Guessing what had happened, she chose the lesser of the two evils before her and leaped
into the mud, which was modestly covering her up to the neck
by the time the door was thrown open in the face of her husband's astonished friend. . . .

Such little happenings brought some variety to the daily
ritual at Bad Nenndorf. Very early each morning I was
awakened by doors opening all down the street. The first morning I had sufficient curiosity to get up and look out of the window to watch the procession of early bathers making their way,
towel in hand, towards the park. Fat, elderly, crippled, they
marched past doggedly, some with the aid of sticks, some with
apparently little the matter with them, determined to take
things in time.

Then the hotel itself began to resound. It was a new concrete
building and far from sound-proof. The few maids I saw

seemed to work from morning till night, never ceasing, and, indeed, Herr Weiss, the proprietor, did the same. He was a thin, anxious-looking little man and his brow was always glistening with sweat. Once, during a breathing-space when he was neither assisting one of the maids with the electric sweeper nor handing round plates in the dining-room, he was moved to confide in me.

"There was a time, Fräulein," he said, mopping his brow, "when I needed only to supervise. Now I must work like a slave. We are allowed very little domestic help, and you can see for yourself it is not sufficient!"

"Why not close some of the rooms?" I suggested.

He looked at me, horrified. "But this hotel is scheduled to serve so many patients, and I dare not refuse them! Sehen-Sie, Nenndorf gets a grant from the State, in order to give members of the Party a Cure at a reasonable price. The doctors must see so many a day, and are forbidden to charge more than so much. The baths themselves cost only one mark a time! Were I to complain, when everyone here is overworked too, I would surely be in trouble!"

A massive woman sat at my table, accompanied by a pale and exhausted-looking daughter. It seemed that the older woman was the wife of a farmer, and terrified lest her crippled limbs should get worse so that she could no longer give even a little help on the farm. As it was, she had had to bring the girl away too, in order to get help in dressing and undressing and to have someone to pilot her to the Baths.

"Yet I cannot sleep at night for wondering how my man is managing things at home!" she confided. "In the old days we had as many farm labourers as we wanted. Now they are always being called up for manœuvres; and just at harvest time too! Nor can we get any girls to manage the cows and help with the livestock. Lise and I must manage it all, somehow, ourselves. The girls, too, are all drafted off to camps nowadays, or to work in the factories. I don't understand it. How can we produce the food we must if we get no more help given?"

I would take my book and my writing things every morning

into the park. There were dozens of inexpensive little cafés and restaurants dotted all over Nenndorf, but the most elegant, the most chic, was the one at the entrance to the park, with its broad terrace from which one might watch the crowds sauntering up and down, apparently carefree, with their mugs of Nenndorf water clutched in one hand. The water was dispensed from a kiosk by another grim-faced woman in long skirts with a glossy bang of hair over her forehead. If you liked, on leaving you could purchase your mug as a souvenir of a healthful experience.

Farther off, past the neat rows of boarding-houses and hotels, were the villas belonging to the resident population of Nenndorf. Painted dazzling white with green shutters, they were surrounded by gardens where late roses cascaded over their wire frames, and where the first asters were beginning to gleam like broken bits of stained glass. And beyond that again was the rich farmland of Hanover. The reaped brown fields rolled towards the horizon, marked off by little patches of pine forest left standing to provide some shade.

Here, on the edge of the country-side, stood the Summer Pavilion of King Jérôme of Westphalia. For this part of Hanover had once belonged to that short-lived kingdom created by Napoleon for one of his brothers. Whether Jérôme, most dissipated and least able of all the Bonapartes, ever actually used it, I could not find out. But its rooms were still draped in Empire crimson or yellow and gold. It now served as a reading-room for visitors taking the Cure, and its massive ebonized tables with their ormolu mountings were used for the display of magazines and newspapers laid out for those who cared to make use of them.

It was too quiet a spot for most of the visitors, and perhaps too far for those who were crippled to walk here. So I found that most mornings I had it to myself. I began to look upon it as my pavilion; mine and Jérôme Bonaparte's. There seemed to be nobody in charge, and one could walk in and out as one liked.

I would set out after breakfast, when the lay population of

Nenndorf was busy with its housework and the patients with their baths and treatment. Even the park was deserted and the neat white streets almost empty. The smell of the great pine forests would meet me before I left the verge of the town. The air from them blew eternally over the fields, across the empty landscape, towards the little coppice of trees giving shade to the pavilion.

Its door would be unlocked already. I would enter what now was the reading-room, and shove aside the magazines spread over the baize-covered table. Except for that utilitarian table, everything must have been more or less as it had been when prepared for Jérôme's own use. The walls were covered with yellow silk and the ceiling sprinkled with stars. A small Empire timepiece stood on a marble-topped table, ticking fussily. And the hours I spent there writing were marked off by its silver chime.

She must have come in so quietly, I never heard her. But I looked up one day to find a woman sitting watching me from the other side of the table. It gave me a shock. She saw that and apologized, speaking in good, if pedantic English.

"Forgive me, I did not realize that you were unaware of my presence. This is my favourite spot, too, when I come to Nenndorf. Here at least one can get away from the eternal Swastika and the canaille."

Without realizing it, I must have travelled far along the route of suspicion and fear; because I caught myself glancing anxiously towards the open windows. She smiled. "Don't worry! There's nobody within hearing. . . . They told me in the town that an Englishwoman was here and used the pavilion every day. So I thought to myself, I will go there and speak a little in the English language for the last time."

"For the last time?" I echoed stupidly.

"Of course. For soon we shall be at war."

She was the first who had said it in so many words. Everyone else, including myself, had buried their heads in the sand. She opened the worn handbag on her lap, drew out a small black cigar, lit it and looked at me over the smoke.

"Don't fool yourself, my dear young friend, nor allow others to fool you either. Have you not noticed the labour shortage, the appeals for thrift, the hurry to get in the harvest? Perhaps it may not come this autumn, after all. But it will come, for all that."

She must have been pretty once and some traces of that still remained. She even wore make-up, a thing frowned upon in the Germany of today. She had belonged to the great world once; one could see that. And yet there was a certain provincialism in her dress, and even in her manner. It was the provincialism of the local aristocrat whose roots are still in the soil. Her tweed suit, which looked as if it had been cut by a London tailor, was now threadbare and old-fashioned. But the pearls round her neck looked real, and there was a small embroidered coronet on the crumpled-up handkerchief lying on the table before her.

"You know"—she smiled slightly—"I have sometimes the oddest thoughts. I find myself wondering how Queen Victoria would have dealt with the situation. If it had not been for Hanover's adherence to the Salic Law, she would have been reigning here as well as in England. Did you ever think of that?"

"But Bismarck deposed the royal family of Hanover," I objected, "and so——"

She smiled again. "Do you think Bismarck would have managed to depose Queen Victoria? I should like to have seen them meet against one another. That would have been something!"

The little clock chimed. The sun, now almost at its height, shone through the slats of the Venetian blinds, casting yellow tiger-strips on the flowered carpet. Except for the breathless ticking of the clock, there was not a sound, either outside or in. It was so hot that even the birds outside had stopped singing.

She said, "This is the calm before the storm."

I was afraid. I turned to Queen Victoria, because I could see that even this woman, oddly outspoken for a German, found comfort in the thought of her. "It *is* a curious thought that she might have come over here constantly; might even have used this little pavilion for the picnic excursions she loved. . . ."

The woman nodded. "Have you been to Bückeburg yet? You must go; it is only a few miles off, and a pretty little provincial town. That was where Queen Victoria's governess, Lehzen, came from. And she obtained such power over her pupil that nobody could combat it until Prince Albert came along. . . . Then she was created a baroness in the Hanoverian peerage and hustled back to Bückeburg. Poor Lehzen!"

I had been to Bückeburg. From Nenndorf the buses radiated in all directions, visiting the sleepy little towns of Hanover. Bückeburg had struck me as being the sleepiest and deadest of them all. From reading the young Victoria's letters I had conceived an aversion to "Dearest Lehzen," but really I was sorry for her. A woman of domineering character, who had raised herself from the provincial life of Bückeburg to a glittering existence at Court, she must have looked with horror at approaching old age spent back in the pit whence she was digged.

But Albert had not brooked so strong an influence beside his own. It must have been he who had worked his young wife round to suggesting that "Dearest Lehzen" had earned a reposeful retirement back in her own home-town. To be created a Baroness would be a poor substitute for Buckingham Palace and the conversation of Lord Melbourne. I knew that Lehzen had found it so, because I had read a very interesting account of how an English clergyman, finding himself in the vicinity, had called on the old lady, and what had transpired during the call.

After a cup of coffee she had invited him to smoke. To smoke in a lady's parlour was unthinkable at that date, and he had been very surprised. He was still more surprised when the Baroness opened a cigar cabinet and begged him to make his choice. Seeing his astonishment, she explained.

She had grown accustomed to informed conversation and could not do without it. Then as now, the educated males of Bückeburg took two hours off at midday, to eat their heavy meals and relax over coffee and a cigar. She stocked up with the finest, most expensive cigars to be had, and then let it be known that they were welcome to come and smoke them at her house. The conversation of the local lawyer, doctor, and pastor would not be up to the level of that of the Queen's Ministers and friends, but it was better than that of their wives. . . .

The woman opposite me took a puff at her own cigar and agreed with me. "I, too, am a little sorry for Lehzen," she remarked, "especially (you remember?) when she dressed in all her finery and went to the railway station to see the train pass by with the Queen and Prince Albert on board, bound for a State visit to Berlin. Of course, she expected it to be stopped, so that she could at least greet her old pupil through the window. Probably she had written to the Queen to say she would be standing there. But the train did not stop."

Then she rose, nodded, and went away, leaving a perfume of cigar smoke to hang about the folds of Jérôme Bonaparte's silk curtains.

29

BECAUSE I was not myself taking the Cure, I was free to visit other little near-by towns besides Bückeburg. They lay dotted about the rich landscape, so embedded in fields that the scent of hay drifted up their narrow cobbled streets. And it was on a hot, heavy afternoon that I entered Celle, in search of any memorials left of the two unhappy women whom history associates with the place.

George the First. Married to Sophia Dorothea of Celle. The words learned by rote long ago as a schoolgirl suddenly took on meaning. This was Celle. This little old town, capital of a vanished Duchy once ruled over by Sophia's father. She had been a pretty, vivacious girl with a turn for satire which hadn't done her any good. Married young to the son of her father's neighbour, the Elector of Hanover, she had been miserable at the Electoral Court. Her boorish and unfaithful husband had neglected her. His rapacious mistress, the Countess von Platen, had humiliated her at every opportunity. No wonder, then, that she had fallen a prey to the charms of the handsome adventurer, Koenigsmark.

There was that midnight drama in the Leineschloss at Hanover. The revengeful von Platen spying on their midnight assignation. The murder of Koenigsmark and the hasty walling up of his body in a chimney of the palace itself. And the hustling back to her father's Duchy of the disgraced Dorothea, where she remained a prisoner for the remaining thirty-two years of her life, in Ahlden Castle, some miles from Celle.

She never saw her children again. Her husband succeeded to the British throne but denied her the title of Queen. Her one hope was that he would die and his son—her son—would release her from this living death. It was known that he had some

sympathy for his mother; that he kept her portrait in his room
with a curtain hanging over it. But she died first, after all.

I wanted very badly to see Ahlden Castle, but heard that it
was in private hands, and the long, breathless summer seemed
to have sapped me of energy enough to contrive anything in
that direction. I remembered the plump, faded aristocrat who
had smoked her cigar beside me in King Jérôme's Pavilion. I
wished I had mentioned the matter to her. It was too late now,
but I felt sure that she would have provided a key.

But I had to content myself with the very graphic description
contained in an old *Life of Sophia Dorothea,* bound in royal
purple, written by W. H. Wilkins at the beginning of the century. He described Ahlden as a "fair-sized manor-house," and
he had been lucky enough to visit the place when the wing inhabited by Sophia still remained shuttered and empty, from the
time of her death. There were, however, no relics or furniture
of hers remaining, since the Hanoverian Government had removed everything in an attempt to obliterate her memory.

Indeed, he told a strange tale of how, some time in the
'eighties of the last century, two boxes containing her private
papers had been found at Ahlden. Orders immediately came
from Hanover to send the boxes there. They had been loaded
on to a farm-cart and despatched to the nearest railway station,
at Reitlagen, to be put on a specified train. On the way to the
station, however, the boxes had mysteriously disappeared. . . .

The sun baked the cobbles under my feet. The old beamed
houses leaned towards each other over my head, and pigeons
straddled on the roofs. Celle couldn't have changed much since
Sophia's day. Now and then, over some inn or ancient building,
one saw a sculptured head of a horse, for this was the centre for
breeding the famous white horses of Hanover. The stud had
been founded by Sophia's son, George II. From it had come the
"cream ponies" which used to draw Queen Victoria's coach.

I turned into an old inn for something to eat. The stone floor
was uneven under my feet. The few little tables were spread
with rough white cloths, and the local postman was having his
glass of beer at the counter. Everyone turned to stare at me, then

turned back to continue their conversation in the sibilant German of Hanover. There was no great air of welcome about the place, for the Hanoverian is surly and dour to strangers. I ate my meal as quickly as possible, then went out again, through streets quietened by the midday hour, and found my way to the empty Ducal palace, gleaming white in the midst of its green park.

It had an oddly Italianate air, and seemed to withdraw itself, foreign to the place. Rebuilt on the site of its predecessor, it reflected the taste of Sophia's father, the last Duke of Celle. He had chosen a Venetian architect to build it, and had brought here the finest artists in stucco work to decorate his ceilings in the Italian style.

I wandered from one cold white room to another. No one else was here at this noonday hour. I had the place to myself. I gazed at the picture of Sophia with flowers in her hair and her dress slipping off one white shoulder; at the engravings of the later Georges who reigned here as well as in Britain; and at the painting of one of the earlier Dukes of Celle reading aloud to his ten children. Then I wandered out again and into the park.

The formal gardens were ringed about by magnificent trees. Something gleamed between their foliage, and I went forward to discover what it was. I found a marble urn, and the sculptured figure of a young woman beside it with a child in her arms. This was the memorial to the second of the two unhappy prisoners of Celle: Carolina Matilda, Queen of Denmark and sister of George III.

A great-granddaughter of Sophia, Carolina's story ran oddly parallel. Brought up as an English princess, she, too, had been sacrificed for dynastic purposes. They had married her off, at the age of only fifteen, to the imbecile young King of Denmark, who had made her the worst possible husband. She, too, had had her life at Court made miserable by the enmity and jealousy of another woman, in this case her mother-in-law. But, Carolina had more intelligence and ability than Sophia. It irked her to see the country misgoverned by a clique of her hus-

band's rakish friends. The King's doctor, Struensee, might not
have been the dashing charmer that Koenigsmark was, but he
had political ideas of his own and a certain ascendancy over his
patient. Was it surprising that he and the Queen should begin
to work hand in hand together?

But the Court Party took fright. The wretched puppet-king
was easily persuaded, not only that his wife had been unfaithful, but that she and her lover were planning to overturn the
State. Struensee was seized and executed, and the Queen might
have suffered the same fate if her brother, George III, had not
stepped in. He promised to keep her a close prisoner if she were
allowed to depart to his Hanoverian kingdom. And there, at
Celle, Carolina Matilda followed the footsteps of her great-
grandmother Sophia, remaining a disgraced prisoner of State.

Not for so long, for she died there three years later, aged only
twenty-four. But the citizens of Celle must have formed their
own ideas of her guilt or had been won over by her charity and
charm. For they promptly named a street after her, and erected
this white marble memorial before which I stood.

It was time to return to Nenndorf. The bus, crammed
already with country people going home, stood in the middle
of the square. One last glimpse of the deserted ducal palace, of
the quiet streets, and gabled houses, and we were in the country-
side again. The haze of this Indian summer lay golden over the
landscape, becoming tinged with a pinkish glow by the time we
reached the little spa. Already the supper tables on the terrace
in the park were full. And when I reached the Hôtel Edelweiss
I could smell the roast pork that was evidently to form the staple
course of our evening meal.

It began (because the day had been warm) with chilled lemon
soup. You have no idea how refreshing chilled lemon soup can
be. Considering the low charge for bed and board, Herr Weiss
fed us extremely well, and the servings were almost overwhelm-
ingly large. One day, privately, he had groaned about that to
me too. How long was he to be expected to provide such quan-
tities of expensive meat, such fruit and vegetables, to his guests,

with food at the price it was? Butter too. Did I realize that now-adays the ordinary German family scarcely ever saw real butter? It was practically commandeered for hospitals, and for hotels which, like his own, catered for the out-of-health, but which had to pay the high market price just the same?

The phrase, "Guns or Butter," had scarcely sunk into my mind then. But his words did make me reflect upon the Government's undoubted anxiety that all who were ailing in Germany today might be restored to health as soon as possible so as to be able to endure whatever might lie before them. . . .

"Is the Fräulein going to the park-concert tonight?" my neighbour asked politely, pushing the large mound of butter in my direction. "It will be a pleasant distraction on so fine a night as this."

I had not thought of it. My excursion had tired me, but the lemon soup had been reviving. I would, after all, take my coffee on the park terrace instead of here. I went out again, joining the stream of guests issuing from all the other hotels, and managed to get a single seat on the already packed terrace.

They had flood-lit the park in honour of this special concert. The grass had turned a dark bluish-green, barred by the stone balustrade before the terrace-café. Sunk deep at intervals, the flower-beds gleamed like jewels. The trees hung over them, dark-green like fountains of emerald, and the band-stand in the middle was spot-lit.

It was not the ordinary little band which played here every afternoon, it was a military band from the summer camp of manœuvres near by. That in itself provided a thrill for the audience. The uniforms of the bandsmen made a little change in the monotonous tenor of the days here in Bad Nenndorf. Besides, it was a local regiment. I could feel local patriotism swelling around me as some of the players were loudly identified by their relations sitting by.

The band played well, as all bands in Germany are forced to do, to escape the wrath and contempt of their audiences. But the *clou* of the performance came half-way through. It was a piece, modern but sounding oddly old-fashioned according to the preference of Germany today, and it had a long trumpet solo in the middle. In order to make this solo the more effective, the trumpeter had been ordered to climb a tree and blow his notes from there.

While the rest of the band worked up to his entry, we watched him climb the tree. A second spot-light appeared, following his progress from branch to branch. That effect was evidently intended to heighten expectation, but I thought it a mistake myself, as his posterior was most often in view, and he was a plump bandsman at that. When he was a short way from the ground and got his bearings and his feet firmly planted, an obsequious private handed up his instrument. Clutching this, he began to straddle out over a limb while the audience watched, breathless, and the orchestral prelude rose to a crescendo, then paused, suddenly, dramatically. . . .

A long trumpet-note sounded over the park. From somewhere beyond the lighted belt of trees, from some decent obscurity in which I longed myself to be, an owl hooted. I held on to myself, trembling; not wanting to be torn alive, a victim on the altar of art, while the solo wavered triumphantly across the flower-beds, blotting out the owl. It ended on a sustained note strengthened by crashing agreement from the band, and I let my own breath go in relief and stilled my impulse to loud, hysterical laughter.

"Fabelhaft!" sighed the crowd.

As the night fell deeper over the park, the coloured flower-beds sparkled more brightly, dimming the stars above. The coffee at the bottom of my cup had grown cold, and the air was now a little cold as well. The band finished up with a Strauss waltz, and presently people left their tables, humming a snatch of the waltz as they went. The park emptied itself into the streets. For a while the streets themselves echoed to voices and footfalls. Then bedroom shutters banged one after another as lights went out.

I leaned over the sill of my room, drinking in the night air. From far off, the owl hooted again and again. It had the whole night to itself. The stars shone so brightly, one knew the first slight frosts of autumn were not far off. But far brighter and harder than they shone the giant swastika perched high above the Bath House, outlined in electric lights which would burn all night.

30

In Hanover itself the statue of Victoria's Uncle Ernest sat grim on his horse opposite the railway station. He was known affectionately to all Hanoverians as "Schwarz Ernst," and the steps about him constituted the chief meeting-place for friends inside the capital or visitors outside. Always there was someone pacing there, waiting for somebody to turn up. I was waiting for no one, but I stood beneath his shadow for a little while, making up my mind what to do next.

Behind me people streamed like ants in and out of the huge station. Above me Schwarz Ernst surveyed his people. The most hated of all the sons of George III, he had been as unsuccessful as Duke of Cumberland as he had been successful here. When Queen Victoria succeeded to the throne and he left England to take over the crown she could not wear, the whole of Britain heaved a sigh of relief. The Prime Minister even advised him to go secretly by night, to avoid unpleasantness. But according to Hanoverian lights, he had made a good king. They did not even resent his English ways, his English staff and coachman.

He knew how to manage them. He told them what to do and they did it. When a few bold spirits, unsettled by what was happening all over Europe during the fatal year of 1848, marched to his palace and asked for a new Constitution, he told them briefly that if he had any more nonsense from them he would go straight back to England and leave them to their own devices. They gave in at once.

Only his niece Victoria never gave in. That matter of the Hanoverian Crown Jewels, for instance. Having originally come from here, he not unnaturally demanded them back. But she would not agree. And he wrote angrily to one of his friends that his niece was appearing at London balls plastered with *his* jewellery. . . .

He may have been right, at that. But he was scarcely right in creating a disturbance at the christening of one of Victoria's children, when he tried to assert his rights as a crowned monarch and to sign the register first, before Prince Albert. According to Queen Victoria's letter on the subject, he was only foiled by Albert giving him "a smart shove," and the whole episode reflects strangely upon the usual decorum of royalty and the times.

I decided to go and have supper at the Café Kropke. Hanover was fuller than usual, because tonight would see the last of the season's illuminations out at Herrenhausen, the country palace of the Guelphs. It had been too good an opportunity to be missed, and I had come in by bus specially to see them. But the bus had brought me in with some time to kill before the festivities started, and the best way to kill it would be over an evening meal.

The Café Kropke was one of the institutions of Hanover. It stood like a small white button-mushroom at a point where many roads met. After the statue of Schwarz Ernst, it was the favourite rendezvous in the city, and most people having met at the first, adjourned to the second. I believe it was destroyed in the Second World War and had been rebuilt along modern lines; but then it reflected an even earlier day and had a Victorian cosiness about it.

The people of Hanover must have been very attached to it as it was, for no attempt had been made to bring it up to date. The little round room was still hung with brocade and stuccoed in white. A three-piece orchestra of aged performers, who looked as if they had been playing there all their lives, discoursed equally faded music, and the elderly waiters greeted nearly every arrival by name.

I took a seat by the window and ordered an omelet bestrewn with that species of fungi which, when cooked, looks like glossy black snails, and which no self-respecting restaurant in Britain would dream of serving, but which tastes so much more delicious than the cultivated market mushroom. I watched the trams radiating from the streets which spread away like the points of a star from the café itself. Presently their lights went up, although there was still a fair amount of light in the sky. I waited until the lights grew brighter and the sky darker, before calling for my bill and going out into the street again.

When the Guelphs grew tired of their dark old palace within the heart of the town, they took the same way that I took out to their summer palace of Herrenhausen. Even now, some country-side still stretched between the two. Straight as a die stretched the road, shadowed by trees. And down it sped a succession of cars and buses, tail-lights winking through the dusk.

There was a greenish light in the sky. As the bus travelled on, it hardened into a flickering line with some dark bulk bearing it up from below. The palace roof had been flood-lit, and when we got nearer, the line seemed to break up, shaping itself into balustrades and pinnacles, with the dark night showing between them. Gradually the whole sprawling outline of Herrenhausen now made itself visible, black as velvet within a rim of fire. The fire seemed to have sprayed its façade with sparks, for the windows were candle-lit, and the glittering chandeliers hanging down from the ceilings within cast up a fountain of light in the middle of every square.

Its gates stood wide open. The bus stopped, and with the silencing of the engine one could hear, suddenly, the roar of traffic still approaching from the direction of Hanover, and the murmur of the crowd elbowing its way into the narrow court-yard beyond. I was swept into the dark stream of men, women, and gaping children; swept round the disappointing frontage of the building facing the road, into a magic landscape stretch-ing before its windows on the farther side of the palace itself.

Here was a park aping Versailles. Before the candle-lit win-dows was a huge, never-ending terrace broken with statuary and balustraded flights of steps. Dazzling white it lay from end to end, and one could see the figures walking on it, picked out so clearly they seemed somehow diminished to the size of perambulating dolls. I became one of them, conscious of the same shrinkage and of the fact that I, too, had lost my shadow so long as I walked here, for the strong arc-lights above us deprived us of that part of our individuality as well.

We were unreal ghosts as we drifted by the windows with their looped-back curtains, their glimpses of huge painted canvases and gilded furniture. We should have worn other garments, belonged to another age. What right had we to be strolling here, pressing our noses against the royal window-panes? As though everyone had become suddenly conscious of this, the crowd began to thin, to trickle down the nearest steps, to lose itself bashfully in the gardens below.

I did the same. It was like entering a chequer-board maze, where the smooth lawns were intersected by vast squares of pink gravel upon which designs had been wrought in coloured stones that sparkled in the unnatural light. Even the lawns themselves were scored with hearts and stars and Prince of Wales's feathers, wrought like Berlin wool-work in the deeper green of ground-ivy closely clipped. This interminable chequer-board seemed to stretch before me, reducing me to the size of an exploring insect. From one design to the next, from grass to gravel, I crawled, dimly conscious of other little figures doing the same.

Until presently the eye became rested again, and the feet halted by the rim of the great basin. This oblong sea of water was hemmed in by arc-lamps too, but at least it showed an uninterrupted surface. Only for a moment, however, until the eye got accustomed to its spaciousness. Then one saw that the water itself was broken up and agitated, making little crescents which caught the light. For the ducks that sailed there so serenely during the day had been disturbed. They shot back and forth agitatedly, every feather gleaming, the light even showing up their tiny paddling feet.

"Look!" a child cried happily, pointing. Some frightened ducklings were sailing by like golden balls. The night, to the birds, must have been hell. Lights and distant music, and all round the rim of that vast basin the echoing voices of the crowd. . . .

I walked round one side of it and then passed beyond, to the wilder reaches of the gardens. Here they had become a park. Few people had penetrated so far, and it was quiet. Quiet under the great trees, though they, too, were illuminated so that every branch sprang out against the stars. Quiet beside the statues which stood brooding with clusters of hidden lights about their feet. The lights sometimes cast shadows over their faces or dark shadows in the marble folds of their garments. Where we ourselves had lost our shadows, they seemed oddly alive.

At the end of a secluded walk, beside a small pavilion, sat the Electress Sophia. She half reclined upon a marble couch on the spot where she had been taken up dying centuries before. Her eyes were turned in my direction. She seemed to be watching me as I drew near. I might have been your subject, I tried to tell her as a reason for intruding upon her solitude. At any rate, my ancestors would have been if you had managed to survive your cousin Anne. At least, we are both British, and a cat may look at a king.

She gazed steadily back at me. The face was fine, thoughtful, aristocratic. A Stuart face, not a Guelph. The face of a strong, ambitious woman who had grown weary waiting for her throne. It was the face of a woman who would have ruled, perhaps as wisely, certainly as autocratically, as the first Elizabeth had ruled. I thought of all the letters the Electress had written to England, to her dear cousin Anne inquiring after her health, and, more openly, less tactfully, to those about Queen Anne, seeking to discover how much longer she would have to wait. But it was her boorish and unpopular son George who had succeeded to the throne of Great Britain, after all. George who had never even bothered to learn his mother's language properly, and who had the German looks and German ways of his father.

I left the Electress to her solitude and began to walk slowly back towards the ornamental gardens again. On one side of me loomed the darkened outlines of the royal stables, left unlit. I had visited them once, during the day. There, in the vaulted coach-house, stood row upon row of equipages, their lamps, their harnesses kept polished as if they might some day ride the roads again. There stood the State Coach of George II, with the Royal Arms of Great Britain on its panels and the White Horse of Hanover as well. The lumbering berlins in which Sophia herself had driven, as well as her miserable daughter-in-law Sophia Dorothea to whom a passage in the State Coach had been denied. The Prince Regent had travelled in them too, when he came over, as he did sometimes, to play at being King of Hanover.

During the height of his unpopularity in England he had even contemplated leaving it for good and taking up residence in this great palace of his ancestors, to be away from the crowds that booed him in the streets. But it was only a momentary whim, and he got over that. He did visit Herrenhausen fairly often, though. And I began to walk towards the outdoor theatre he had planned, where he had watched performances on just such a warm, late summer night as this.

The stage was a lawn of turf raised high above the rest. Where the footlights had punctuated its rim, cascades of water fell down below into giant shells of bronze. The wings were formed of hedges of clipped yew, and the dark leaves formed a background to the golden statues standing in a double row face to face, receding away from the audience. The whole setting glimmered in peacock colours under its skilful lighting, and the golden statues echoed the cascades which, streaming with golden light, fell into the dark shells beneath.

But the stage was empty; the Regent and his successors gone. Their passing had not been so long ago, after all—well within living memory. The Kaiser's only daughter had married the Duke of Cumberland, who should have been King if Hanover had still been a kingdom. As it was, he had inherited the private property of the Guelphs. Behind those lighted palace windows still stood the buttoned, late-Victorian suites of furniture with which the rooms were furnished according to the Kaiserin's taste. Terrible taste it was, running to a particular shade of electric blue. The Prince Regent would have been horrified.

It was almost time to go home. The fountains shot up, wavering, in colour as a last gesture to the visitors. The biggest fountain of all, the biggest fountain in Europe, sent a long wavering plume towards the stars. "Herr Jé!" breathed the crowd, watching it. And there must have been a little wind after all, or at any rate a breath of air, for the rash spirits who had gathered on the wrong side of the basin to admire it suddenly shrieked and ran, soaked to the skin by its spray.

There came a burst of fireworks. The golden rain showered down on the terrace; the burning stars and Catherine wheels soared above the basin, to fall down, hissing, towards the water and further alarm the ducks. The last great blaze went out in the sky. Now the lights were going out gradually all over the park and gardens. Gradually, so as to give us warning that the fête was finished. First one great tree, then another white statue, was blotted out. The lights went out round the basin, and the frightened water-fowl suddenly ceased their cries. The lights went out on the terrace. The lights behind the windows blinked a little in sympathy, then went out too. And the roofline of the Herrenhausen dimmed and faded slowly as if the whole building had taken a step back into the past of the Electress Sophia and the Prince Regent themselves.

Dazed, we bumped into each other, passing through the gates. The line of buses stood ready, their engines running. Mine was a Special Excursion from Nenndorf (four hours in Hanover; the Fire Fête at Herrenhausen, and return to Nenndorf at midnight), and I found myself sitting beside the farmer's wife who sat at my table in the hotel.

"Herrlich!" she sighed, turning to me. "So beautiful, it even made me forget my problems. Tomorrow, alas! I go home to find them waiting for me. The cow-milking . . . the shortage of helpers . . . my man so overworked and in need of the holiday they tell him he must not take!"

The bus moved forward. A faint gleam of magic still travelled with us at first, but gradually disillusion set in. The words of my companion found an echo which, after some brooding, was given utterance by another passenger who had evidently gathered courage from the obscurity.

"We all have our problems, nicht? Such things cannot be cured by a few fireworks!"

I WAS surprised, that summer, at the wave of church-going which broke over Nenndorf and the surrounding district each Sunday.

My German acquaintances were surprised by it themselves. Never before, it seemed, had so many people gone to church so regularly. Then I would see them starting out themselves, perhaps a trifle shamefacedly if they were not in the habit, and joining the streams of people making towards the churches of different persuasions scattered throughout the town.

The farmer's wife and her tired, pale daughter invited me to go to the Lutheran Church one Sunday. On our way we passed the Catholic chapel. Its doors stood open, and we could see the silent, packed crowd leaning against the pillars within. Another crowd, made up of those who had arrived too late to find seats, clustered about the doors and spread like a great fan over the graveyard beyond.

"One can understand the Catholics, since, after all, it is obligatory for them to go," said the old woman, stumping painfully along, "but we Protestants here in Germany are not usually so devout."

"Yet here we are," said her daughter, "though I don't believe we know why. It is as if some wind were blowing us to church."

The church, too, was full by the time we reached it. But the old woman squeezed doggedly into the last pew, managing to make room for us there as well. The doors, too, had been left open because of the heat. And the wave of psalm-singing halted passers-by on the road, so that some of them left it and blocked up the entrance still more.

An old man with a face like parchment stood up in the pulpit. He preached about Naboth's vineyard. Presently his voice became strong and authoritative. I could follow only a little of his discourse, but the farmer's wife gave me the whole of it later. It was a remarkable sermon, and the people listened to it, their faces turned towards him, as still as stones.

He said that the kingdom ruled over by Ahab was a theocracy, whose kings were required to swear that, where the state laws came into conflict with those of God, they would uphold the latter. On the surface, the King's wish to unite Naboth's vineyard with the rest of the royal gardens, to which it lay adjacent, seemed reasonable enough, and his offer of the full value in money or land elsewhere was just. It was, in fact, a rearrangement of property which, from the practical point of view, would have benefited everyone all round.

But Naboth had moral objections. He said, "The Lord forbid it me, that I should give the inheritance of my fathers unto thee." And the King, in his disappointment, went home and turned his face to the wall.

Then entered his Queen, Jezebel. And Jezebel, being a foreigner, did not understand the Constitution of the country which the King had sworn to uphold. She taunted her husband with weakness, and then set about having Naboth killed so that the vineyard came, after all, into the King's possession. But Elijah the Prophet, encountering Ahab in the stolen vineyard, cursed him saying, "In the place where dogs licked the blood of Naboth shall dogs lick thy blood, even thine."

What made the prophet so angry? It was not so much the murder of Naboth, as the breaking of the King's coronation oath to uphold the moral rights and freedom of the individual. At this point the preacher became still more solemn as he pointed out that those who acquiesced in the destruction of these rights—who defied the old moral code and who handed their consciences over to others to keep—were actually tearing down with their own hands the only bulwarks of protection they had between themselves and the State.

His sermon was listened to in an intense silence. When the last words were uttered and the Benediction given, everyone filed out without a word or a look at his neighbour. The heavy midday air seemed to strike us as we entered the grave-

yard and went down a narrow lane between hedges, back to the
town. And the larks sang with indifference, mere specks in the
sky above.

Half-way down the lane the farmer's wife stopped to rest and
to mop her brow with a large Sunday handkerchief. Her
daughter spoke then, uttering the first words we had had between us since leaving the church.

"That Pastor is a brave man," she said. "I doubt he will not
be left among us for long."

Her mother nodded. "I should like to shake him by the
hand."

That afternoon the park was as full as usual, and the terrace
café was crowded. The band played beneath the trees whose
tops were becoming tinged with yellow. I had chosen a seat
close by the terrace balustrade, and could watch the crowd,
picking out those members of it whose appearance had become
familiar. There passed the honeymoon couple, arm-in-arm.
There went the old man in the bath-chair, propelled by his
puffing and florid daughter. Nearly everyone seemed to belong
to the respectable lower middle-class, dressed in its Sunday
clothes, enjoying this day of leisure from treatment as well as
from work. Family groups shouted greetings to one another,
and all the people seemed to converge from the side paths towards the wide central one leading towards the band-stand and
the music.

As the music sucked them into the centre of the park, one
noticed more clearly the few figures left on its outskirts. Near
me, to my left, I now caught sight of a tall, elderly man in a
shabby coat of vaguely ecclesiastic cut, sitting alone on one
of the park benches. His head was inclined a little, as if he were
listening to the selection from *Lohengrin* being played by the
band. But he made no attempt to walk nearer and join the
crowd. Once, momentarily, he turned and looked at the terrace,
and I saw it was the Pastor, for I recognized that noble face.
And I watched to see if anyone would stop and greet him. Now
and then a few figures still hurried past that bench, on their
nearer way to the music. I watched their feet falter, saw their

hurried half-turn in search of another path. Then, since there was none, their defiant continuance and their shamed passing by without even a half-nod of recognition.

There was no doubt that the farmer's wife would have done the same. But the sight was painful to watch, and so I turned my head and looked down upon a group just passing beneath me. They walked with distinction and a slight arrogance which divided them from the loud-voiced, rotund figures around them. One of them glanced up at me as she passed, and I saw it was the cigar-smoking woman of the Pavilion. Our eyes met, but hers slid away so quickly I could not be quite sure if she had really recognized me or not. She had been indiscreet in her conversation, so I dare say she was right.

But for the first time I faced the fact that the invisible circle drawn round the Pastor was drawn round me too.

Only some strange lethargy of the spirit still chained me to Nenndorf. I had already tasted spa life in Germany; seen all I had come to see. The friendly old woman and her daughter returned to their farm. The season was beginning to draw to its close. A few of the hotels had already put up their shutters. Each night the stars burned with a colder brightness, and the beech trees growing around Nenndorf were tinged with metallic brown. And yet I put off returning to Britain. The signs were no more ominous than they had become lately every autumn after the harvest was gathered in. I had that feeling that if I anticipated the worst, the worst would come.

There were two new arrivals, however. Two young Englishmen taking a holiday, on their way home after having been engaged on some special work with a big firm of shipping engineers in Copenhagen. They nodded to me across the Speisezimmer of the Hôtel Edelweiss, and presently we would stop and talk to one another if we passed each other out of doors. It was they who gave me enough impetus to pull out and cross the Channel at last.

Our paths had crossed in the park. We met a little distance from the domed kiosk where one of the hard-faced women of Lower Saxony dispensed the spa waters in thick grey mugs.

There she stood in the shadow of the stone roof, with her un-becoming bang of hair across her forehead and her long coloured skirts, looking like some medieval piece of sculpture between two of the stone pillars supporting the canopy above.

From here, one just heard faintly the clatter of the mugs being pushed across the marble counter and the chink of pfennigs being laid down on it in payment. The breeze which fanned her skirts was bringing down the leaves already. They whirled down the paths towards us, and the creaking of the boughs above our heads punctuated the faint rhythm of the band.

"Getting a bit late in the season," said one of the young men.

"Oh, I don't know," I said, "it's rather pleasant yet."

"Maybe." He shrugged his shoulders. "All the same, my friend and I think it's about time we were going home."

His tone was significant. "There's been the same feeling in the air every autumn for years," I said rather defiantly. "Always at the last minute something happens to calm things down. But I've seen everything here, anyway. I was thinking of going to Hamburg and from there crossing over to Denmark by the train-ferry. I like Denmark."

The other boy shrugged his shoulders. "Please yourself," he said. "That is, if you don't mind risking being interned."

"Nonsense!" I said, still struggling. "Besides——" (here I remembered something someone had told me, encouragingly, about Denmark. Actually, I had remembered it all the time. It was what had led my thoughts to going there in the first place.) "Besides, I'd be able to get home from Denmark no matter what happened. The Harwich–Esbjerg crossing was kept going right through the last war, wasn't it?"

A party of stout Germans drifted by, gazing at us curiously, each right hand uplifted, clutching a mug. They looked like children on some fantastic picnic. We suddenly stopped talking about war.

"Have you seen the Bouquet Well?" the first boy asked politely. "We've just been. It's jolly queer. All those old bouquets."

I hadn't. A dozen times I had set out to go to it and then been sidetracked by something else. But now there was that sense of hurry. One more thing to see, and then I really would leave Nenndorf. . . .

I said good-bye and walked across the park towards the opposite gate. This led away from the town to the gentle uplands surrounding it. I had hardly reached the park gate, however, when hurried footsteps sounded behind me. It was the taller of the two young English engineers. He drew alongside me and I stopped. He looked around cautiously, making sure that no one was within hearing.

Then he said, "We've been having a bit of an argument as to whether I should tell you or not. Don't pass the word on or we'll get into trouble."

"What word?" I asked.

"Well—you know we've been working in Copenhagen for over a year. Meeting other engineers, the shipyard people and so forth. And I can tell you this. If anything *should* blow up suddenly, there'll be no going home after the war has started. Not by the Esbjerg route, anyway. They're closing that."

"Thanks," I said. "Yes, maybe I *will* go home."

I went on slowly, rearranging my plans in my head. I went on towards the Bouquet Well, for at least there was time to see that. It was late afternoon now, and the road was empty. I saw the low stone rim of the Well set in the middle of an open space. A few bushes ringed it round at a distance, and the grass was trodden flat by the feet of visitors come to see this local curiosity.

I leaned down and looked into the waters of the Bouquet Well. They were impregnated with some mineral which acted as a preservative to anything dropped in. For generations, brides had come here on their wedding-day and had flung down their bouquets, so that years later they could bring their children to see the never-fading flowers.

Presumably the Well was sometimes cleaned out. Otherwise the flowers would have risen in a tight mass to the top long before. And yet I could read quite clearly, embroidered in gold on the broad satin ribbons, dates of many years before. The flowers floated with their stalks down. Perhaps they had been weighted before being flung in. Anyway, the bunches of pale roses, the sheaves of lilies, the florists' arrangements, and the simple, home-made sprays all looked up at me in one gigantic bouquet, unfaded, like a circular mosaic.

It was the elaborate ribbon bows about their stems which gave the thing away. Otherwise one might have thought the petals still were soft and fragrant. But the satin looked metallic, like gilded metal parings. And they never moved or undulated in the water....

I turned away, thinking how small yet exquisite a thing this was, to set beside the glories of Europe I had seen that year. I could not know that when the Unter den Linden was dissolved in rubble and the famous white Zwinger had become merely a dream of vanished Europe, those frozen bouquets of coloured flowers would be among the few things which remained.

THE END